The Glacial Geology of Holderness

AND

The Vale of York.

THE
GLACIAL GEOLOGY

OF

HOLDERNESS

AND

THE VALE OF YORK

BY

SIDNEY MELMORE

Printed for Sidney Melmore, 61 Carr-lane, Acomb, York, by T. Buncle & Co. Arbroath.

1935.

Indeed, I am, perhaps wrongly, inclined to look upon all geological theories as having their being in a mythical region, in which, with the progress of physics, the phantasms are modified century by century.

Letter of A. de Humboldt to J. L. R. Agassiz.

PREFACE

This book contains things old and new.

The glacial geology of Holderness has been the subject of research for a hundred years. The investigators of the middle period are yet remembered; but the work of the pioneers is apt to be forgotten. Particularly would this seem to be so in the case of Sedgwick. The earlier chapters of the book may help to recall his work.

That which is new is an extension, in part, of a paper read before the Geological Society of London, which was in due course published; and, in part, of observations communicated to the Yorkshire Geological Society, which were not published.

The examination of the gravel deposits at Holme upon Spalding Moor was suggested to me by my friend Mr John S. Gayner. I would not have embarked upon that work had it not been for the assurance of his kindly interest and encouragement. This book, also, owes much to his criticism and advice. I offer my thanks to him.

The relation between the direction of valleys and joint planes, which is at the base of the argument in Chapter XXVI, is simple and direct. It can be verified by anyone possessed of a prismatic compass.

In the course of my work I have had the benefit of Mr. J. W. Stather's intimate and long-standing acquaintance with the district. To Mr. C. N. Bromehead and his colleagues in the York office of the Geological Survey, I am under obligation, both in their official capacity as authors of the recent Memoir on the Geology of the District around Huddersfield; and individually, for help in the identification of erratics. Mr. J. A. Dell has given me much valuable material for the study of contemporaneous manganese deposits. I am indebted also to Mr. K. P. Harrison for help both in the library and in the field. To these gentlemen I express my thanks; and also to Miss E. Holmes, Librarian to the Yorkshire Philosophical Society, who has given me much valuable assistance in searching for old records.

SIDNEY MELMORE.

YORK, November, 1924.

CONTENTS

THE GLACIAL GEOLOGY OF HOLDERNESS.

CHAPTER I.

THE DILUVIAL AGE.

The diluvial rubbish . . . . —ADAM SEDGWICK, 1825.

Over a great part of Yorkshire, and of many another part of the world in both hemispheres, there may be noted today " widely extended masses of incoherent materials separating the vegetable soil from the solid strata."

The scientific study of these deposits began over a hundred years ago; and now, to any one wishing for a better knowledge of them, than he already possesses, it is a great advantage to recall some of the passages in which the pioneers in this study put down their views of these beds, so incoherent!

And by good fortune, I can commence with an extract from the writings of Sedgwick, in which he draws an illustration from the district it is my object to consider in the light of to-day. The passage is from a paper published in April 1825 in *Annals of Philosophy.*

" The existence of widely extended masses of incoherent materials separating the vegetable soil from the solid strata of the earth is a fact which forces itself upon the attention of every practical geologist. These materials have for many years been divided into two classes. The first composed of a series of deposits originating in such causes as are now in daily action. The second composed of various materials irregularly heaped together, often transported from considerable distances, and supposed to have originated in some great irregular inundation. . . .

" Prof. Buckland was, I believe, the first geologist who adopted the terms *diluvium* and *alluvium, diluvial detritus* and *post-diluvial detritus* to designate the two classes of phenomena above alluded to. . . .

" All the principal vallies of England exhibit in their higher portions occasional examples of nearly horizontal deposits of comminuted gravel, silt, loam, and other materials accumulated by successive partial inundations. The nature of these *alluvial* deposits and the cause of them are so obvious, that it is unnecessary to refer to particular instances. If we descend from the hilly and mountainous regions and examine the courses of our rivers near their entrance into any widely extended plains, we frequently find their banks composed of incoherent materials of a new character. They are not made up of thin layers of comminuted matter formed by successive inundations, or of silt and turf-bog accumulated in stagnant waters, but of great irregular masses of sand, loam, and coarse gravel, containing through its mass rounded blocks sometimes of enormous magnitude. It is at once evident that the propelling force of the rivers is entirely inadequate to the transport of such materials as these. We may observe, moreover, that they are not confined to the banks of the rivers, but spread over all the face of the country, and often appear at elevations many hundred feet above the level of any natural inundation. To such materials as these the term *diluvial* (indicating their formation by some great irregular inundation) is now applied by almost all the English school of geologists.

" The rivers which descend from the western moors and unite in the great central plain of Yorkshire, afford a succession of beautiful illustrations of the appearances which have been just described. While rolling from the mountain chains, and uniting with their different tributary branches, they leave masses of alluvial matter in every place where the form of the valley admits of such a deposit: and after passing through the inferior regions and escaping through many ravines and gorges into the great plain of the new red sandstone, they then find their way through enormous masses of *diluvial debris* which often mask the inferior strata through considerably extended tracts of country. If we follow any of these rivers into the central parts of the great plain, we may still find (with occasional interruptions) the *diluvial detritus* descends with the surface of the ground, often forming the channel of the waters, and, where the level of the country admits of it, sometimes surmounted by an accumulation of newer *alluvial* materials. By the ordinary action of the waters, the two distinct classes of deposits sometimes become mixed and confounded; but I have never seen an example where their order is inverted, or where, through any extent of country they alternate with each other. The instances adduced are not exceptions to, but examples of, the general rule. There is not, I believe, a single river in England which does not afford a more or less perfect illustration of some of the phenomena above described."

The inadequacy of rivers as a propelling force continued to be felt, and the presence of these " rounded blocks sometimes of enormous magnitude " constituted an unsolved problem to geologists for a further ten or fifteen years.

CHAPTER II.

AGASSIZ AND THE GLACIAL THEORY.

You have made all the geologists glacier-mad here, and they are turning Great Britain into an ice-house.

LETTER OF EDWARD FORBES TO J. L. R. AGASSIZ, 1841.

Those who, like myself, had to struggle with the Boulder-clays and northern drift more than forty years ago, without the aid of glaciers and icebergs, and with no clear theory of the changes of level of land or sea, were apt to leave out of our local descriptions phenomena which seemed merely perplexing, or merely exceptional. Yet we attempted, even then, to express some ideas of the succession among diluvial beds; and we now recognize in the full descriptions of the cliffs of Yorkshire and Norfolk the facts which we had seen as clearly, but had not been able to enunciate in language suited to their importance, or conformable to modern theory.

JOHN PHILLIPS, 1868.

Jean Louis Rodolphe Agassiz established the glacial theory which was destined to supersede the diluvial hypothesis. Its inception was, however, due to others, as is clearly shown in the following passage taken from his *Life and Correspondence* edited by E. C. Agassiz (vol. I, 1885, p. 260).

" The summer of 1836 was an eventful one for Agassiz—the opening, indeed, of a new and brilliant chapter in his life. The attention of the ignorant and the learned had alike been called to the singular glacial phenomena of movement and transportation in the Alpine valleys. The peasant had told his strange story of boulders carried on the back of the ice, of the alternate retreat and advance of glaciers, now shrinking to narrower limits, now plunging forward into adjoining fields, by some unexplained power of expansion and contraction. Scientific men were awake to the interest of these facts, but had considered them only as local phenomena. Vanetz and Charpentier were the first to detect their wider significance. The former traced the ancient limits of the Alpine glaciers as defined by the frame-work of debris or loose material they had left behind them; and Charpentier went farther, and affirmed that all the erratic boulders scattered over the plain of Switzerland and on the sides of the Jura had been thus distributed by ice and not by water, as had been supposed.

" Agassiz was among those who received this hypothesis as improbable and untenable. Still, he was anxious to see the facts in place, and Charpentier was glad to be his guide. . . . He went expecting to confirm his own doubts, and to disabuse his friend Charpentier of his errors . . . he came away satisfied that a too narrow interpretation of the phenomena was Charpentier's only mistake."

Through the advocacy of William Buckland, Professor of Geology in the University of Oxford, the glacial theory promulgated by Agassiz became familiar to the geologists of this country.

CHAPTER III.

THE DILUVIUM OF HOLDERNESS.

The diluvium of Holderness is of great interest, partly from its immediate connexion with a series of operations which have affected all the neighbouring districts; partly also from its occupying the whole line of coast, and from its enormous thickness, which enables us to examine with detail all the circumstances appearing to throw light upon its history.

ADAM SEDGWICK, 1825.

If we make allowance for the error of the diluvialists in believing that water (and not ice) was the transporting agent, their accounts of field observations remain of value today.   We may therefore continue with Sedgwick as our guide : —

" In many places where it occupies a succession of lofty cliffs, it puts on a rude appearance of stratification, or at least may be subdivided into separate masses which possess distinct characters.

" The lower part of the cliffs, to the height of about twenty feet, generally consists of a stiff bluish clay, which in many places passes into a dark brown coloured loam.   Through the whole of this mass are imbedded an incredible number of smooth round blocks of granite, gneiss, greenstone, mica slate, &c., &c., resembling none of the rocks of England, but resembling specimens derived from various parts of the great Scandinavian chain.   Irregularly mixed with the preceding are found, in perhaps still greater abundance, fragments of carboniferous limestone, of millstone grit, of lias, of oolite, and of chalk, torn up from the regular strata of the country, and driven into their present situation by a great eastern current which has left its traces on every part of the neighbouring district.   In regard to the imbedded fragments abovementioned, two things appear to deserve notice. 1.   They exist in equal abundance in the upper as well as in the lower portions of the diluvial loam.   This fact, though difficult of explanation, has been remarked in other similar deposits, and seems to prove the gigantic nature of the forces by which the materials have been drifted into their present position. 2.   The boulders derived from distant countries are rounded by attrition; but those which are derived from neighbouring rocks are little altered in form.   The hard Norwegian rocks are smooth and spheroidal, but the fragments of oolite and lias, and still more the fragments of chalk, are often sharp and angular.

" Over the preceding deposit come a set of beds of sand and comminuted gravel, very variable both in their structure and in their thickness.   They seem to have been formed by a longer continued and a less violent action than that which produced the diluvial loam on which they rest.

" Over the sand and gravel we may sometimes find traces of ancient turf-bogs and of other alluvial deposits, formed in situations which were once in the interior of the country; but are brought into their present position by the encroachments of the coast.

" Lastly, over all the preceding we find in many places a considerable thickness of blown sand.

" Such are the phenomena exhibited in the cliffs of Holderness."

And later in the same paper he remarks—" The great unformity in the mineralogical character of the rocks in many parts of Cumberland often prevents us from ascertaining the direction in which the diluvial boulders have been drifted from their native beds. This difficulty we do not meet with in following the blocks of Shap granite, as they cannot be confounded with any other rocks in the north of England. It has already been stated that they almost cover the ground in many places near Shap; and that they have been lifted over the escarpment of the carboniferous limestone, and drifted over the hills near Appleby. I may now add, that they have been scattered far and wide over the plain of the new red sandstone—that they have rolled over the great central chain of England into the plains of Yorkshire—that they are embedded in the diluvium on both banks of the Tees—and that a few straggling blocks have, if I mistake not, found their way to the eastern coast."

The paper from which this account is taken was published by Sedgwick in the *Annals of Philosophy* for July, 1825.

We may say, therefore, that before the end of the year 1825 the following facts had been noted regarding the glacial drift of Holderness. 1. It is capable of subdivision into separate masses which possess distinct characters; 2. It consists in part of a stiff bluish clay and a brown loam; 3. Rocks of Scandinavian origin occur in it; 4. Shap granite had been transported from Westmorland over the Pennines to the central plain of Yorkshire and to the coast.

CHAPTER IV.

THE BOULDER CLAYS OF HOLDERNESS.

*Again, too much faith is apt to be placed in lithological differences as indi-
cating differences of age, as if one and the same bed of till would not neces-
sarily have different sets of stones embedded in it in different parts of its
extent. Lastly, the same may be said about colour as a test of age.*

J. R. DAKYNS, 1879.

*To give a complete catalogue of all the varieties of pebbles which lie in this
clay, would be a work of great labour and little interest. Such comparisons
are important only in proportion to the light they throw on the probable direction in which the waters moved, that transported them to their present localities; and this object is better attained by selecting a few well-defined rocks,
than by gathering loads of ordinary specimens.*

JOHN PHILLIPS, 1829.

The brown loam recognised by Sedgwick as a distinct component of the Holderness drift was termed the Hessle Clay by S. V. Wood, junr., and the Revd. J. L. Rome, in 1868.   This name was given to it on account of its very full development near Hessle, on the Humber. They describe it as differing from the Purple Clay in " being more earthy, less tenacious, and its foxy red colour being variegated by cinereous partings.   Its best characteristic, however, is the presence in it of irregular-shaped fragments of chalk, not abundant, but sufficiently so to make a marked contrast with the chalkless upper portion of the purple clay on which it so frequently rests."   Wood and Rome also described another clay at the bottom of the series as " a lead-coloured clay abounding in chalk debris, accompanied by stones and boulders from all sorts of rocks."   They named this the Basement Clay.   It is more sandy than the Purple Clay; of a greenish-blue colour, and often contains masses of green loamy sand with shells.   These included shelly masses were described by Sedgwick, in 1826;[1] and afterwards became known as the " Bridlington Crag."

Wood and Rome's classification may be compared with that of Sedgwick as follows : —

SEDGWICK, 1825	WOOD AND ROME, 1868.
Ancient turf-bogs and other alluvial deposits.	Lacustrine marls with *Cyclas.*
	Gravel, principally chalk.
Sand and Gravel.	Sands and Gravel.
Dark brown loam.	Hessle Clay.
	Hessle Gravel.
Stiff bluish clay.	Purple Clay.
	Sand and Gravel.
	Basement Clay.

In 1885, Clement Reid split the Purple Clay into an Upper and a Lower division, the line of separation being a red band of obscurely stratified boulder clay material about a foot thick, sometimes replaced by a few feet of gravel.

The classification had now been developed into the form in use at the present time ; but it is interesting to note that the various Boulder Clays were identified merely by the colour of their ground-mass.   Clement Reid evidently had an inkling of the way in which the classification could be placed on a firmer basis, for on page four of his memoir *The Geology of Holderness,* published in 1885, he remarks : —

" At present we cannot say that any of the far-transported rocks are confined to the higher divisions, though Shap Granite is at any rate more abundant in the Purple Clay, and may be entirely wanting in the Basement Clay."

The development of the method whereby the Holderness Boulder Clays can be identified by their contained erratics was the work of J. W. Stather, the results of which he announced in his Presidential Address to the Yorkshire Geological Society delivered on December 8th, 1928.[2]

[1] *Annals of Phil.,* vol. xi, 1826, p. 339.
[2] *Proc. Yorks. Geol. Soc.,* vol. xxi, 1929, p. 151.

After collecting large quantities of stones from each of the Boulder Clays, he was able to tabulate his results thus : —

BOULDER CLAY	CHARACTERISTIC BOULDERS.
Hessle, ...	Cheviot porphyrites and Silurian grits.
Purple, ...	Carboniferous rocks, Whin Sill, Lake District rocks, Chalk, and Lias.
Basement, ...	Rhomb-porphyry, augite-syenite, and elaeolite-syenite, of Scandinavian origin.

" It must be clearly understood," he says, " that in applying the test to any section, it is the wide group of rocks of ascertained origin, and not merely an individual from such a source which is significant of the horizon. Individual erratics do not count, for the possibilities are boundless that a sporadic specimen of any type of erratic may occur anywhere in the series." Rhomb-porphyry, for example, having been introduced into the district at the earliest period, may be redistributed and occur again in any of the later boulder clays.

More recently W. S. Bisat[3] has still further sub-divided the boulder clays. His sub-divisions are made solely on the basis of colour; their systematic importance remains to. be proved by experience.

CHAPTER V.

THE BURIED CLIFF AND RAISED BEACH AT SEWERBY.

Inland a continuation of the same high Chalk Wolds, trending southward, defines the Holderness plain, and marks by its abrupt eastern margin the position of an ancient buried and degraded sea cliff . . . Geologically, Holderness is the district between the ancient cliff and the sea.

CLEMENT REID, 1885.

In the winter of 1883, a fisherman noticed some bones in the foot of the cliff at Sewerby, and by reporting the matter to G. W. Lamplugh, his observation led to one of the most important discoveries ever made in the history of Yorkshire Glacial Geology. These bones were excavated by J. R. Mortimer. Clement Reid, who was at that time carrying out the official Geological Survey of the district, was informed of the discovery by Mortimer; whereupon he carried out excavations sufficient to enable him to present the earliest printed description of the occurrence in his Memoir on the *Geology of Holderness*, published in 1885.

Two years later, further work was carried out under the auspices of the Yorkshire Geological Society, the results of which were communicated to the British Association in 1887 by J. W. Davis. Finally,

[3]*The Naturalist*, 1932, p. 215.

a committee was appointed by the British Association to investigate the matter. Its report, drawn up by G. W. Lamplugh, appeared in 1888,[1] and contains the most detailed account of the deposits and their relation to one another.

At Sewerby the Chalk disappears from the coast-section, which south of this point displays nothing earlier than the glacial deposits.

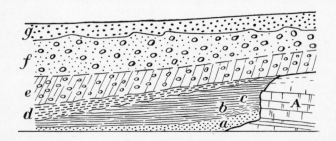

Fig. 1.

SECTION SHOWING THE BURIED CLIFF AND RAISED BEACH AT SEWERBY
(after G. W. Lamplugh).

A. Chalk.   a. Raised Beach.   b. Land wash.   c. Blown sand.   d. Chalky rubble.
e. Basement Boulder Clay.   f. Upper Boulder Clay.   g. Gravel.
The horizontal line at the bottom of the figure represents the present sea-level.

It was the discovery of the true nature of this abrupt change which gave rise to the activities which have been briefly indicated above.

The excavations at Sewerby disclosed the existence of a cliff 30 or 40 feet in height with an ancient sea-beach at its foot, both buried in glacial drift and other deposits.

The chalk floor close to the cliff was found to be at about the level of the present high-water mark. On this floor lay the beach deposit, 3 to 5 feet thick near the foot of the cliff and increasing in thickness southward. The base of the beach is at about 7½ feet O.D., according to E. R. Matthews,[5] and the top is somewhat above the present high-water mark. It consists of chalk pebbles, with pieces of flint occasionally; and more rarely there were found pebbles of basalt, granite and other igneous rocks. Here and there among the gravel occurred the bones of mammals, birds and fish; and sometimes the shells of the periwinkle, oyster and other molluscs, while many of the chalk pebbles were perforated by the borings of *Pholas, Saxicava* and *Cliona*.

Above the beach was a rain-wash deposit of marly clay with masses of fallen chalk and streaks of drifted sand. This clay was about 5 feet thick where it touched the cliff. Fragments of birds' bones and many small land-shells were found in this bed.

Overlying this old land surface came a great mass of clean yellow wind-blown sand, extending right up to the top of the old cliff, and

[1] *Rept. Brit. Assoc., for* 1888, (1889), p. 328.
[2] In W. H. Crofts, *Trans. Hull Geol. Soc.*, vol. vi, 1906, p. 58.

having a thickness of fully 25 feet in places.   A few more bones were found near the base of this deposit.   The sand contains the same type of minerals as the North Sea Dirft of East Anglia.

We have now reached the top of the buried cliff and accounted for some 40 feet of deposits.

At this height the excavators encountered a layer of chalk-rubble. On top of the cliff it was about a foot thick, but as it passed outward over the blown sand it was found to thicken rapidly to about 12 feet, while at the same time the base of it descended to at least 20 feet above sea-level.   Almost everywhere throughout the district this chalk-rubble is found at the base of the glacial drift, the Basement Clay resting upon it.   But at the point where the excavations were made it differs somewhat from the normal type, being more earthy, and containing fewer shells and fewer boulders.   The top of the Basement Clay is here well marked by a thin seam of fine shingle and sand, which, when traced southward, is found to develop into a thick bed of finely laminated clay, with a seam of fine gravel above and below it.   The Basement Clay is followed by another boulder clay of a brownish colour, which Lamplugh considered to be the Purple Boulder Clay.   Finally, at the top of the section there was a bed of gravel 10 feet thick.

Thus the Sewerby excavations provided patent evidence of an ancient sea-beach raised somewhat above the present shore-line and backed by a chalk cliff now buried under glacial deposits; and above it an old land surface lying beneath the oldest known boulder clay in Yorkshire.

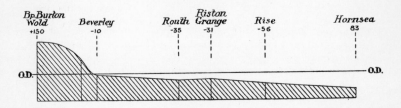

Fig. 2.
SECTION THROUGH THE SUB-GLACIAL PENEPLAIN OF HOLDERNESS.
(Vertical scale 53 times the horizontal).

Once this was known, it was a simple matter to confirm the existence of the marine peneplain underneath the whole district of Holderness, and to determine the westward and southward course of the buried cliff with the help of borings already put down in search of water.   A typical section through Holderness, constructed in this way, is shown in fig. 2. By this means Clement Reid traced the buried cliff through Bridlington, Driffield, Beverley and Cottingham, to Hessle where it is broken through by the Humber; thence southward down to Ludborough in Lincolnshire.

Before passing on to examine the evidence at Hessle, it will be convenient to close this chapter with the list of fossils found in the

Sewerby excavations, as given by Lamplugh (*Q.J.G.S.*, vol. XLVII, 1891, p. 411) : —

VERTEBRATA.

Elephas antiquus Falc.
Rhinoceros leptorhinus Cuv.
Hippopotamus amphibius L.
Cervus (?*megaceros* Hart).

Bison sp.
Hyaena (*crocuta*, var. *spelaea* ?) Goldf.
Arvicola amphibius L.
Birds.

Gadus morrhua L.

LAND MOLLUSCA.

Helix hispida L.
Helix pulchella Mull.
Pupa marginata. Drap.
Zua subcylindrica L.

MARINE MOLLUSCA.

Purpura lapillus L.
Littorina littorea L.
Ostrea edulis L.
Mytilus edulis L.
Pholas and *Saxicava*, indicated by borings.

CHAPTER VI.

THE BURIED CLIFF AND RAISED BEACH AT HESSLE.

I am not aware that any remains of land animals have occurred in this rubbly deposit, near Flamborough, or on the wolds; but at Hessle it contains the teeth and bones of the extremities of horse, ox, and deer, very little worn by attrition. These bones, therefore, belonged to animals residing in the neighbourhood.

JOHN PHILLIPS, 1829.

The buried beach at Hessle has been exposed to view on two or three occasions. In 1868 Phillips[1] published some field notes made over forty years previously, recording mammalian remains, and sands and gravels which he suspected were of marine and fluviatile origin. Clement Reid, also, in his memoir gives a section and records the discovery of bones, but so far no marine shells had been found. It was not, indeed, till 1906 that indubitable proof of marine conditions was forthcoming, thanks to the observations of W. H. Crofts. The following description is taken largely from his paper,[2] and the account given by T. Sheppard.[3]

Immediately to the west of the railway station at Hessle the trace of the marine peneplain was seen at a height of 20 feet O.D., or 8½ feet above the present high-water level of Spring Tides. On this lay an unstratified mass of shingle consisting of chalk pebbles up to a foot in size, some bored by *Cliona*. There were, too, a considerable number of rolled flint cobbles, but no foreign stones were noticed. This last point has been remarked by both Crofts and Sheppard. The gravel contains numerous fragments of *Cardium* and *Tellina*.

[1]*Q.J.G.S.*, vol. xxiv, 1868, p. 250.
[2]*Trans. Hull Geol. Soc.*, vol. vi, 1906, p. 58.
[3]*Geological Rambles in East Yorkshire*, 1903, chap. xx.

Above the gravel came beach sand 3 inches thick and upwards, with fragments of the same shells, overlain by more sub-angular and rounded chalk gravel up to 11 or 12 feet thick. Over all lay 12 or 14 feet of boulder clay having, according to Crofts, the appearance of the Hessle and Purple Clays; and being, according to Sheppard, the uppermost of the three Yorkshire boulder clays, that is to say the Hessle.

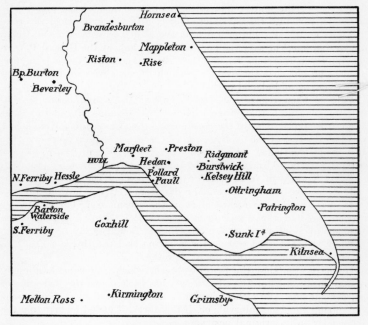

Fig. 3.
MAP OF SOUTH-EAST YORKSHIRE.
(Scale : ⅛ inch to 1 mile).

Sheppard, in his book published in 1903, gives the following list of mammalian remains found in these gravels : —

> *Equus caballus* (the horse).
> *Cervus elaphus* (red deer).
> *Cervus tarandus* (?) (reindeer).
> *Elephas* sp. ? (probably mammoth).
> *Rhinoceros* sp. ? (rhinoceros).
> *Hyaena* sp. ? (indicated by gnawings only).

Five years later he contributed the following important note to *The Naturalist*, 1908, p. 424 : — " In re-examining the collection of mammalian remains from the pre-glacial gravels at Hessle, near Hull, in the Hull Museum, which I obtained some time ago, I find there are the humerus, radius and ulna of a reindeer (*Cervus tarandus*). They are from the

angular chalk gravel which occurs below the boulder clay, and exhibit
no signs of having been water-worn.   Some pieces of antler from the
same bed are probably of the same species, but owing to their fragmentary condition, positive determination was not possible.   The
record appears in *Geological Rambles in East Yorkshire*, marked with a
' ?.' The bones now recorded, however, place the presence of the reindeer at Hessle in pre-glacial times beyond doubt.''

And there the matter has stood from that time to the present.

Let us look into the case more closely. In the first place, the reindeer does not make its appearance in the glacial sequence till the Upper
Mousterian age,[4] or say, the end of the first half of the Glacial Period.
The inference therefore is, not that the reindeer at Hessle is of pre-
glacial age, but that the gravel in which its remains were found is not
older than the mid-glacial period.

Can we then regard the Hessle end of the raised beach as contemporaneous with the Sewerby end?   No remains of reindeer were
found at Sewerby, despite the careful investigations made at that place.
Nor does the rest of the evidence tend to reconcile the discrepancy. The
only shells mentioned as occurring at Hessle, namely, *Cardium* and
Tellina, were not found at Sewerby, and contrariwise none of the shells
found at Sewerby have been recorded at Hessle. The superincumbent
boulder clay are also different. The Basement Clay overlies the Sewerby
beach, but there is no record of it in the accounts of that at Hessle;
instead, we find the direct deposition of the Hessle Clay, with the
possible intercalation of some of the Purple Boulder Clay.

There are thus good reasons for believing that the Hessle gravels are
not contemporaneous with those at Sewerby.

We have seen that the Sewerby beach, which, following Lamplugh,
we may speak of as of Sub-Glacial age, lies little above the shore-line of
this present age. So either there was no differential movement of the
land during this long interval; or, if there was, it ended by bringing the
land nearly to its original position.

Whether any such movement did take place we shall see in the next
chapter.

CHAPTER VII.

THE RAISED BEACHES AT EASINGTON AND KIRMINGTON.

*All geologists who have examined the exposure [at Easington, Co. Durham]
. . . are agreed that it is undoubtedly a littoral formation and although there
may not yet be complete agreement as to the exact age or extent of this deposit,
yet there can be no question that it must be taken into account in any discussion of Glacial and Post-Glacial formations of the East of England.*
                                                    DAVID WOOLACOTT, 1922.

[4]W. J. Sollas, *Ancient Hunters*, 3rd ed., 1924, p. 214.

There is, indeed, one deposit among those which I have examined, and only one, which at first sight seems to suggest inter-Glacial conditions. This is the estuarine silt or warp of Kirmington in North Lincolnshire, at from sixty to eighty feet above present sea-level which . . . is closely associated with true Glacial deposits, and marks a pronounced alternation of some kind.

G. W. LAMPLUGH, 1913.

In 1920, David Woolacott published a preliminary description[1] of a raised beach at Easington, four miles south of Seaham Harbour. Two years later, he wrote a fuller account.[2]

The main features of the deposit are as follows : —

The beach rests on a horizontal platform of Magnesian Limestone at about 60 feet above sea-level. In one direction it is seen to pass off the rock floor on to a true boulder clay. This boulder clay is the Main or British Drift of Woolacott's classification, equivalent to the Purple Clay of Yorkshire. The deposit is at least 15 feet thick. It consists of a lower and upper portion. The lower portion is made up of loose sand and large pebbles, many of them bored by *Saxicava*, *Cliona* and *Polydora*, and containing many shells, both whole and in fragments. The upper portion consists of horizontally-bedded and firmly-calcreted conglomerate with few shells.

The Mollusca occurring in the deposit include : —

*Littorina littorea.	Buccinum undatum
L. rudis.	Cyprina islandica.
*L. obtusata.	Mytilus edulis.
*Patella vulgata.	Ostrea sp.
Purpura lapillus.	Rhynchonella psittacea.

Saxicava sp.

The commonest species are marked with an asterisk.

The beach gravel is not overlaid by true boulder clay, but by re-assorted boulder clay, the whole being covered by washed soil.

In seeking traces of a similar raised beach in other parts of Eastern England, Woolacott considered briefly the remarkable deposit at Kirmington, in Lincolnshire.

This estuarine bed at Kirmington was first described by Wood and Rome in 1867,[3] in the following words : —" This deposit consists of a brick-clay interbedded with sands, and capped by a thick bed of large, rounded, or beach-rolled flints. The clay has yielded some horns of a *Cervus*, and also the estuarine or littoral mollusca, *Scrobicularia piperata* and *Mytilus edulis*."

With the progress of glacial research, the importance of the Kirmington bed became fully realised, and a Committee of the British Association was formed to examine it minutely. The following particulars are taken from its Report,[4] published in 1905.

[1] *Geol. Mag.*, 1920, p. 307.
[2] *Ibid.*, 1922, p. 64.
[3] *Q.J.G.S.*, vol. xxiv, 1868, p. 156.
[4] *Rept. Brit. Assoc.*, for 1904 (1905), p. 272.

By putting down a boring, the solid Chalk was reached at sea-level, corresponding with the marine peneplain considered in the last two chapters. The full sequence was as follows : —

		Ft.	Ins.
	Surface Soil (at 95 ft. O.D.), ...	1	0
A.—	Clay with foreign stones, ...	4	0
	Well-worn shingle, principally of battered flints, ...	8	0
B.—	Laminated warp with estuarine shells, and at its base a thin seam of peat associated with a sandy warp containing freshwater shells in one part of the pit, ...	18	6
	Clean yellow sand, with pebbles of chalk and flint, ...	4	9
	Red clay passing downwards into tough reddish-brown clay, ...	7	6
C.—	Purple clay, streaked with silt and loam, passing downwards into tough purple clay with small stones including some erratics, ...	10	6
	Stoneless purple clay, ...	5	0
	Stoneless yellow clay, ...	6	0
	Flinty gravel, ...	4	6
	Yellow clay and loam with small drift pebbles, ...	5	0
	Yellow sand, full of well-rounded quartz grains and specks of chalk, ...	8	0
	Yellow sand and laminated clay, ...	4	0
D.—	Tough compact lead-coloured clay, with a few small foreign pebbles, ...	5	3
	Tough yellow clay streaked with chalk, ...	1	0
	Solid chalk and flint, ...	3	0
		96	0

The base of the all-important bed B is thus at **64 feet O.D.**, and the bottom of the clay A, capping the raised beach deposit, is at 90 feet O.D.

From the laminated warp B, Clement Reid recorded the following shells : —

Scrobicularia piperata.   *Cardium edule.*
Hydrobia (Rissoa) ulvae.   *Mactra subtruncata.*
Tellina balthica.   *Mytilus edulis.*

He also examined the plant remains from the underlying peat and found them to indicate sub-arctic estuarine conditions.

The erratics in the overlying clay A included basalt, porphyrites, rhomb-porphyry, grits, etc.

The purple clay C resembled the Purple Clay of Holderness in general appearance. Chalk and flint greatly predominated in it, but the following rocks were also found, namely, Red Chalk, black flint, Spilsby Sandstone, ferruginous pebbles, quartz, basalt, and porphyrites.

The clay D was hard and tough, and very different from A and C, both in texture and colour, being in the latter respect like the Basement Clay of Holderness. The pebbles in it were smaller than those in C, and there was a still higher proportion of chalk and flint. Among the erratics were basalt, poryhyrite, sandstone, black flint grit, quartz, etc.

In discussing the Kirmington deposit, Woolacott remarks : [5] " Above

[5] *op. cit.*, 1922, p. 71, footnote.

it is a well-worn beach shingle, principally of battered flints and a clay
with foreign stones.   Is this clay a true boulder clay?   Is it Hessle
clay?   If so, it is the equivalent of the Durham Prismatic Clay and
other reassorted clays which are not of direct Glacial origin."

The clay A, above the beach-shingle, contains pebbles of Cheviot
porphyrite, and is undoubtedly the Hessle Clay.

The height and age of the Kirmington Raised Beach is the same
as that at Easington.

CHAPTER VIII.

THE SPEETON SHELL BED.

*Northward there is an ancient littoral deposit in Speeton Bay. . . It con-
sists of silty sand and mud, very similar to that of Kirmington.*

CLEMENT REID, 1885.

Both the Easington and Kirmington beds are indubitably raised
beaches, and either of them is alone sufficient to prove that at some time
between the Purple and Hessle glaciations the land stood about 80 feet
lower in relation to sea-level than it does at present.

As to the condition of affairs in Yorkshire, some have supposed that
erosion of the coast has removed all traces of a high-level beach; while
others have pointed to the well-known shell bed at Speeton as evidence
of such.

This bed was discovered by Phillips in 1855 and will be found
described in all its essential particulars in the third edition of his
Geology of Yorkshire. It was subsequently examined in greater detail
by G. W. Lamplugh,[1] and by the Kirmington Committee of the British
Association,[2] who give the following section : —

		Ft.	Ins.
	Boulder Clay, ...	45	0
	Fine chalky gravel, ...	1	6
Estuarine	Yellowish sandy silt with shells, ...	6	2
Shell-bed.	Black silt, ...	4	0
	Black silt with sandy streaks and a little gravel, ...	2	0
	Fine gravel, chiefly of chalk, ...	4	0
	Speeton Clay.		

The shell bed is thus 17 feet 8 inches thick and rests on the surface of
the Speeton Clay at a height of approximately 86 feet above the present
beach. This surface is not flat, but slopes landward at an angle of 25
degrees.

[1] *Geol. Mag.*, 1881, p. 174.
[2] *Rept. Brit. Assoc., for* 1906 (1907), p. 313.

Attempts to trace the bed southward failed, but northward it could be followed for a distance of fifty yards.

According to Lamplugh, the 45 feet of boulder clay is made up thus:—

		Feet.
C.	Reddish Boulder Clay, ...	30
B.	Sand and Gravel, ...	5
A.	Dark Boulder Clay, ...	10

The clay A, he at first thought was the Purple Boulder Clay, but later[3] he considered it to be the Basement Clay; the red clay c, being the northward extension of the Hessle Clay.

The distribution of the mollusca is shown in Lamplugh's section:—

	Ft.	Ins.
Fine chalky gravel, ...	0	6
Dark clayey sand; few shells. Soft yellow sand with indurated lumps: many shells, *Cardium edule*, *T. balthica*, *Scrobicularia piperata*; passing into, ...	9	2
Dark blue-black muddy sand, with a foetid odour; with a few pebbles and plates of Kimmeridge shale: many shells—*T. balthica*, *C. edule*, *Utriculus obtusus*, *Hydrobia ulvae*, plentiful; *Littorina littorea* and *L. rudis*, rare; at the very bottom—*Mytilus edulis*, ...	5	1
Gravel of Red and White Chalk, broken Neocomian fossils, etc., ...	1	6
	16	3

In all, the following species were obtained:—

Tellina balthica.	*Mytilus edulis.*
Psammobia sp.	*Littorina littorea.*
Mactra sp.	*L. rudis*, var.
Scrobicularia piperata.	*Hydrobia ulvae.*
Cardium edule.	*Utriculus obtusus*, var. *pretenuis.*
Rhynchonella psittacea.	

The height of the Speeton shell-bed accords with those at Easington and Kirmington; the main obstacle in the way of correlation is the fact that the bed is overlain by the Basement Clay. If this clay is properly *in situ*, then the mollusca in the bed below it should show some resemblance to those in the Sewerby deposit. The fauna in the latter is, however,, so meagre that comparison is rendered difficult; but it may be legitimate to take into consideration the shells found in the Basement Clay of Holderness.[4] All the six shells in Lamplugh's list occur in Bell's table from the Basement Clay except *Ostrea edulis*. The species in the Basement Clay is, according to Bell, *O. celtica*, not *O. edulis*.

Of the eleven Speeton shells, only *Littorina littorea* occurs in the Sewerby beach; but six occur in the Basement Clay, namely, *T. balthica*, *Mactra* sp., *M. edulis*, *L. littorea*, *L. rudis* and *U. pertenuis*. The record of *C. edule* in the Basement Clay is noted by Bell as " very doubtful; perhaps from Speeton."

[3] *Q.J.G.S.*, vol. xlvii, 1891, p. 407.

[4] A list of 180 molluscs from the Basement Clay, with critical notes by Alfred Bell, will be found in *The Naturalist*, 1917, pp. 95-98 and pp. 135-138.

Six species are common to both Speeton and Kirmington, namely, *T. balthica*, *Mactra* sp., *S. piperata*, *C. edule*, *M. edulis*, and *H. ulvae*.

Five species are common to both Speeton and Easington—*T. balthica*, *M. edulis*, *L. littorea*, *L. rudis*, and *R. psittacea*.

Scrobicularia piperata and *Hydrobia ulvae* do not occur in the Basement Clay, but both are found at Speeton and also at Kirmington.

Thus the faunal evidence suggests that the Sewerby beach is not of the same age as that at Speeton.

As to the faunal lists of Easington, Speeton and Kirmington, there is a satisfactory measure of agreement, such differences as exist being no doubt due to geographical distribution.

The opinion held by Lamplugh in 1881 regarding the Speeton bed was that " the shells confirm the idea strongly suggested by the shape of the ground that the beds were formed at the mouth of a quiet tidal estuary." Later in life he rejected all high-level shell-beds as evidence of interglacial submergence, except that at Kirmington. He preferred to interpret them as fragments of a sea-bottom pushed upward into their present position by the advancing ice.

But it is clear that a fragment of the Sewerby beach with a portion of its superincumbent Basement Clay, pushed up 80 feet would not yield a deposit resembling the Speeton shell-bed; and the Sewerby deposit is the only Sub-Basement Clay beach of which we have any knowledge.

The main difficulty connected with the Speeton beds is overcome if we conclude that the shell-bed is really *in situ*, the Basement Clay lying above it having alone been pushed into its present position. The above considerations lend support to this conclusion.

CHAPTER IX.

KELSEY HILL.

. . . to make known a very remarkable locality well deserving of further research, and which has an important bearing upon some questions still under discussion.

JOSEPH PRESTWICH, 1861.

In 1828 Phillips examined a large excavation about a mile south of Ridgmont, close to Burstwick, from which gravel had been obtained for road metal. He described the place in the first edition (1829) of his *Geology of Yorkshire*. " Sand, pebbles and marine shells of comparatively recent, and water-worn fossils of more ancient date, are here mixed together, in confused and irregular layers. The pebbles and fossils may be clearly identified with the chalk and flint of the wolds, the lias of the coast near Whitby, the magnesian limestone near Sunderland, the coal and limestone series of west Yorkshire, as well as the greywacke and other slate rocks, with porphyry, granite, &c., of Cumberland and Westmoreland.

"Amidst this heterogeneous mass, which indicates such various and violent currents of water, it is remarkable that we find many rather delicate marine shells, in tolerable perfection. Besides the strong shells of *Turbo littoreus, Purpura lapillus*, and *Buccinum undatum*, we have *Mya arenaria, Tellina solidula* and *tenuis, Mactra subtruncata* ?, *Cardium edule*, and a shell which appears to me to be *Crassina scotica*. The mass descends to a great depth, and is found beneath the adjacent marsh-land, which consists of fine clay, lying upon peat and trees, and is part of an extended level tract, reaching from the Humber near Pattrington, almost to the sea, at Sandley mere. It seems to have been, at some former period, a channel for some vast volume of water; for it winds as other vallies do, and the gravel hills which bound it are abrupt on the concave side, and slope gently down on the other.

"In the cliffs against the Humber at Paul, very similar phenomena are observed. The gravel and sand are here remarkably contorted, and intermixed with alternating layers of a sediment much like warp. The shells are of the same kinds as in the pit near Ridgmont, similarly arranged, and equally plentiful. The pebbles and fossils, mixed with them, are all very similar, but the masses are generally very small, and flint is more abundant, a circumstance probably depending on the proximity of the chalk wolds."

Prestwich[1] visited the district in 1860. He has nothing to add to Phillips' account of the gravels at Ridgmont, except the important observation that *Corbicula (Cyrena) fluminalis* occurs therein.

From Ridgmont he proceeded to Kelsey Hill. As his is the first published account of this well-known locality, it will be of interest to give his own description of it.

"The section at this spot is extremely interesting. It exhibits great beds of coarse gravel and fine shingle interstratified roughly and irregularly with beds of sand—the whole of a light colour, and with much oblique bedding. In places there are no shells; in other places they are most abundant. . . .

"The gravel in the upper beds consists of subangular flints with pebbles of the older rocks, but the latter are in far larger proportion in the lower part of the section, some beds consisting almost entirely of small boulders of granite, greenstone, quartz, porphyry, mica-slate, limestones, lias, and hard chalk, together with very large flints. They are almost all worn and sub-angular, and many are perfectly rounded. Some specimens are above a foot in length. A few of the limestone blocks retain faint traces of glacial scratching. Many of the blocks of chalk are drilled with Annelid borings and perforated with the holes of the *Pholas crispata*."

The shells collected by Prestwich were examined by J. Gwyn Jeffreys, and it then appeared that none of them were in their original habitat. The *Corbicula*, for example, "being a freshwater shell, must either have been washed out of an older deposit or else carried out to sea from the rivers which it inhabited." The question then arose whether the shells were all contemporaneous and of the same date as the gravel. "With one or two exceptions," says Prestwich, "I am inclined to answer in the affirmative."

His main quest was in search of evidence to prove that boulder clay lay under the *Cyrena* gravels. Being unable to find such evidence at Kelsey Hill, he went to Paull to see the river-side section described by Phillips. "I there found several of the same shells (including the *Cyrena*, but in much fewer numbers and more broken) in beds of sand with but little gravel, reposing upon an irregular surface of grey clay; but, this clay containing no boulders or fossils, I could not feel certain about its being the Boulder-clay."

Not to be beaten, he had a boring made at Kelsey, and excavations carried out at Paull.

The boring at Kelsey failed in its immediate object, but yielded the following information : —

BORING AT KELSEY HILL.

	Feet.
Sand and gravel with shells, ...	4
Large gravel, ...	16
Smaller gravel, ...	8
Larger gravel in grey loam (Boulder-clay ?), ...	8
	—
	36

The excavations at Paull were successful and showed the section : —

SECTION AT PAULL CLIFF.

	Feet.
Soil and silty gravel, ...	8
Sand and gravel with shells, ...	12
Sandy dark-coloured clay without stones, ...	6
Clay with stones (Boulder-clay).	
	—
	26

He concluded, then, that " these gravels with the *Cyrena fluminalis* overlie the great mass of Boulder-clay of Holderness."

He also availed himself of the following boring put down at Old Pollard Farm : —

BORING AT OLD POLLARD FARM.

	Feet.
Soil, ...	2
Red brick-clay, ...	4
Black warp, ...	34
Red clay full of stones, ...	20
Rough gravel with sand and spa-water, ...	26
Very fine clay, clear of stones, ...	8
Bed of flint, ...	2
Black Moor, decayed wood, ...	2
Blue clay with white sand, ...	1
Blue clay with white marl, ...	8
White marl-clay with small cobbles and flints, ...	9
Chalk with bed of sand, ...	5
Chalk clear of flint, ...	69
	—
	190

His remarks on this boring and his final conclusion are expressed in the following words: "Here beds of gravel occur low down in the Boulder-clay. The upper three beds belong probably to the alluvial deposits of the marshes. The stony clay beneath representing the Boulder-clay, would, if continued on the same level, range under the Kelsey Hill sands and gravels, which therefore, so far as superposition is concerned, might form an upper member of this series. But the gravel is more worn and more shingly than is usual in the mass of Boulder-clay. It has more the character of beach-shingle; for not only have we littoral shells, but rounded blocks of chalk, pierced by Annelids and the *Pholas crispata*, are also common. These are features which I did not notice in the coast-section; nor have I there observed, in those thick beds of sand, the fine lamination and large oblique bedding. These may be owing to the nearer proximity to the mouth of the old river. Further, I found in the coarse gravel of Kelsey Hill pebbles of limestone showing glacial scratches more or less obliterated. These facts therefore afford grounds to view the Kelsey Hill gravels as partly reconstructed beds, deriving some of their materials from the lower beds of the Boulder-clay and associated gravels. The worn and irregular state of the surface of the Boulder-clay at Paull Cliff also gives some support to this partial denudation of the lower beds of the Boulder-clay before the end of that glacial period."

CHAPTER X.

KELSEY HILL (Continued).

Of course there are wide-spread divisions, implying great lapse of time and great changes of condition; . . . But it is not every wretched patch of gravel, or every eroded surface of a till that has this meaning.
                                                J. R. DAKYNS, 1879.

In Wood and Rome's paper already referred to in a previous chapter, little is added to Prestwich's description of Kelsey; but they record at least 15 feet of Hessle Clay overlying the gravel. They also recognised the 20 feet of red clay full of stones in the Old Pollard Farm boring as being Hessle Clay. They agree with Prestwich that the gravel at Paull, "which rests on the purple clay," seemed identical with that at Kelsey.

We pass on now to consider Clement Reid's contributions to our knowledge of these deposits.

In his day the Kelsey Hill pit was not in good condition, but he was able to confirm the fact that boulder clay overlies the gravel. An adjoining pit, which he examined, "showed at the north end a perfectly clear face of boldly current-bedded shingle and sand of about 40 feet, without any trace of Boulder Clay. On the west side, also about 40 feet high, and close to Kelsey House, a purple chalky Boulder Clay overlies the Gravel, resting most irregularly on it.　This disturbance is probably, in part at least, subsequent to the deposition of the Boulder Clay; for a fresh-water alluvial deposit in one place fills a basin in the Gravel lined with Boulder Clay, and is apparently contorted with it.　This Boulder Clay sweeps down towards the marsh both south and east of Kelsey Hill farm, its base descending from 50 feet above the sea to about 20 feet in a quarter of a mile."[1]

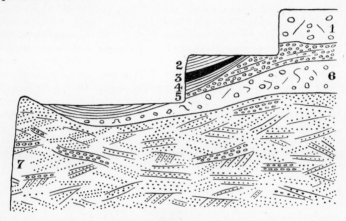

Fig. 4.

CLEMENT REID'S SECTION AT KELSEY HILL.

1. Stony brick-earth.　2. Blue clay.　3. Peaty bed.　4. Blue clay.　5. Earthy gravel.　6. Boulder clay.　7. Gravel.

The fresh-water bed overlying the boulder clay was apparently formed in a pond about 50 feet wide.　The peaty clay was full of plant remains— pond-weed, reed and water-crowfoot—which throw no light on the climatic conditions; but he makes the very shrewd remark: "This Fresh-water Bed must have been formed when the submergence was about 40 feet, for it rests partly on porous gravel, and water could not remain in the pond unless the line of saturation were 40 feet higher than now."[2]

As to the Paull gravels, Reid agreed with previous observers that they are an extension of those at Kelsey.

In 1909, T. Sheppard and J. W. Stather[3] published an important paper on a new pit situated just north of the old one at Kelsey Hill. Serial sections showed that "the core of the hill consisted of a conical gravel mound, similar to those at Keld and other places nearer Bridlington, which had been over-ridden, kneaded out, and generally disturbed by an advance of the ice, which plastered the sides with boulder clay and filled in any irregularities of the surface with the same material.

[1] Geol. of Holderness, 1885, p. 55.
[2] op. cit., p. 75.
[3] Proc. Yorks. Geol. Soc., vol. xvi, 1909, p. 171.

" The direction of this movement was obviously from the north, from which point also came the water which gave a current-bedded structure to parts of the gravel."

They found the gravel included pebbles of augite-syenite, rhomb-porphyry, basalt and Carboniferous Limestone; together with Liassic, Oolitic and Chalk pebbles. A few Scottish rocks were also detected.

As an appendix to this paper the authors give a list of forty-six invertebrates. It includes all the Kirmington species of mollusca.

It is noteworthy that the only boulder clay mentioned by Sheppard and Stather is " of the foxy-red Hessle type, and contains few boulders, which are generally of small size, and of which a very considerable proportion consists of Cheviot rocks." It has already been mentioned that Wood and Rome considered the boulder clay in the Old Pollard Farm boring was also the Hessle Clay. It is possible, therefore, that the Purple Clay seen by Clement Reid resting on top of the Kelsey Hill gravel, is not really *in situ*.

As to the nature of the boulder clay underlying the gravel, Sheppard and Stather remark that " while this is in all probability the ' basement clay,' it is of course difficult to decide by a core from a boring." The first-named author has since stated that the gravel rests upon purple boulder clay.[4] According to Wood and Rome, the same is true of the gravel at Paull.

The base of the Kelsey Hill gravel is not seen in the pits. Clement Reid has stated that the boring put down by Prestwich was begun on the floor of the pit, and that, therefore, it showed the base of the gravel to be at least 30 feet below sea-level.[5] We shall return to this matter in a later chapter. Meanwhile, it can be said that the gravel of Kelsey Hill is of later date than some of the Purple Clay, and older than the Hessle Clay; and that the upper part of it, which alone is available for inspection, has been over-ridden by the ice, and partly incorporated in the moraine of that glaciation.

This moraine can readily be traced along the line of low hills from Kelsey northward to Brandesburton. But Kendall and Wroot[6] have shown that this line of hills does not mark the most westerly position of the Hessle ice. East of Driffield lie the lacustrine and morainic deposits of Craike Hill, and south of Middleton on the Wolds are two truncated spurs clearly marking the extreme position of the ice-front. There are, however, no truncated spurs further south. The water flowing along the ice-edge from Craike through Middleton ran thence through that channel cutting the Wolds from Kipling Cotes to Market Weighton.

Here, then, we may take leave of Holderness and pass to the consideration of the Vale of York.

4*Trans. Hull Geol. Soc.*, vol. vii, 1927, p. 28.
5*Geology of Holderness*, 1885, p. 66.
6Kendall, P. F., and H. E. Wroot, *Geology of Yorkshire*, 1924, pp. 811-812.

CHAPTER XI.

THE VALE OF YORK.
THE FOUNDATIONS.

An observer stationed on the swelling margin of the eastern wolds, at an extreme height of eight hundred and five feet, or on the steep escarpment of the oolitic moors, which rise to one thousand four hundred and eighty-five feet, may look to the westward over a uniformly low plain or vale, which from the Tees ranges southward across the Ouse, Wharfe, and Dun, and is, with some variation of character, prolonged parallel to the Trent as far as Nottingham.

Through all this extensive course, it is flanked on the east by lias clays and limestones, which are themselves overlooked by parallel walls of oolite and chalk, and on the west by a regular terrace of magnesian limestone. From one end to the other it is underlaid by red and coloured clays and sandstones, which, by some ancient devastations of water, have been deeply and irregularly excavated into subterranean valleys, and again overspread by vast heaps of transported materials.

JOHN PHILLIPS, 1836.

Here, with a few strokes, Phillips presents us with a brilliant sketch of the solid geology of the Vale of York.

Let us now trace the surface of the Keuper Marl—the " red and coloured clays "—and the Bunter sandstone, and locate some of the subterranean valleys of which he speaks. To do this we must avail ourselves of the records of borings and well-sinkings, of which many are given in the Geological Survey Memoir on *The Water Supply of the East Riding of Yorkshire.*

At the village of Huby, three miles south-east of Easingwold, 25 feet of drift had to be penetrated before the Keuper Marl was reached at 65 feet above sea-level. South-west of Huby, the village of Newton upon Ouse stands on 73 feet of the " diluvial rubbish " resting on the surface of the Bunter sandstone at about 20 feet below sea-level. At Kirk Hammerton, still further to the south-west, we find the surface of the Bunter has risen to approximately 36 feet above sea-level, the drift being 24 feet thick. Continuing in the same direction, we reach Hunsingore, and find the sandstone forms a hill standing 125 feet above the sea.

We can now draw a section across the buried valley, along the line just traversed. The result is shown in fig. 5*a*.

Another section, further south, is seen in fig. 5*b*.

The bottom of the valley in the neighbourhood of York is at about 35 feet below O.D. At Bilbrough the Bunter rises to 120 feet above the sea and then begins to fall again to the west, until, at Tadcaster it is about 20 feet below sea-level. Fig. 5*c* shows a third cross-section, still further south. The valley-bottom we have been tracing has here

sunk to −80 feet O.D. On the west side it is bounded by a low ridge—
buried under 90 feet of drift—separating it from another valley, the
bottom of which is at least 70 feet below sea-level.

In this way the buried valley can be traced seaward, through
Barmby on the Marsh through Goole and Read's Island, where it is
about 85 feet below the sea.

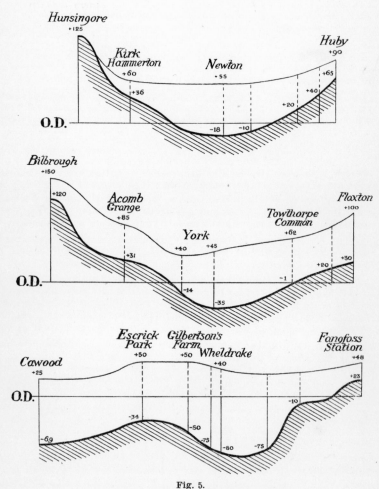

Fig. 5.

SECTIONS ACROSS THE VALE OF YORK.

Showing the eroded surface of the Trias beneath the Drift.

CHAPTER XII.

THE PLAIN.

The diluvial rubbish is spread out almost uniformly over the central plain.
ADAM SEDGWICK, 1825.

Having traced the form of the base of the diluvium, we may now turn to examine the topography of its upper surface, with the help of a 1-inch contour map.

The 100-foot contour-line defines the limit of the plain.

After running along one side, it reaches Northallerton, and then turns southward.   Within the space described, the ground rises here and there above 100 feet between Northallerton and Topcliffe; but at such places the Trias is often found at or near the surface, and provides a sufficient explanation of the anomalies.   But between Topcliffe and York, a distance of nearly twenty miles, the average height of the plain does not exceed 60 feet above sea-level.

The course of the 100-feet contour-line southward from Thirsk is in no way remarkable until Claxton is reached.   Here we note the beginnings of a change in the topography.   The contour-line indicates a spur projecting into the plain in a south-westerly direction as far as Gate Helmsley, where, after a slight decline, the ground rises again to form the ridge on which the village of Holtby stands.   Following the trend of this ridge on a 6-inch map, we find it marked by ground rising above 100 feet, as at Kimberlow Hill, near Grimston, and at Siward's How, close to the Friends' Retreat, on the outskirts of York.

South of this ridge, the plain continues.   Here its average height is not more than 40 feet above sea-level, and the 50-feet contour-line suffices to indicate, with even greater clearness, the existence of another ridge.   It runs from Stillingfleet eastward through Escrick Park to Wheldrake; and after crossing the river and reaching the village of Sutton upon Derwent, we find it again, running north to High Catton, where it reaches a height of over 100 feet above the sea.

We have already noted, at the beginning of Chapter IV, how, in order to trace the direction of the " diluvial currents," Phillips advocated the selection of a few well-defined rocks and recording their distribution.   He chose Shap granite, Carrock Fell gabbro, and the Brockram as his characteristic rocks.

" Eastward from Shap Fells, this granite has been rolled by the towns of Orton and Brough toward the hollow in the great summit ridge at Stainmoor, on the top of which pass the blocks remain, to attest the direction and force of the transporting waters.   From this point the granitic boulders seem to have been dispersed in different directions; as we find them in Teesdale, at Cotherstone, below Barnardcastle near Greta Bridge, and Darlington, at Scotton, south of Rich-

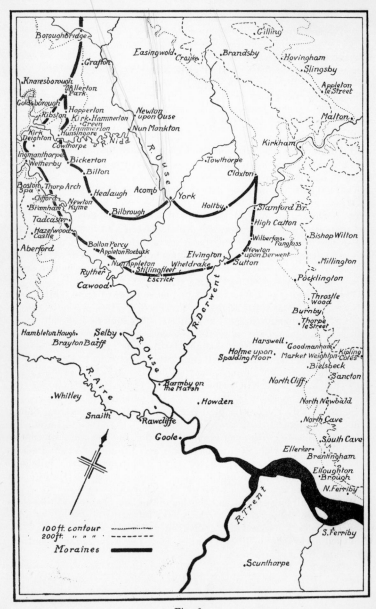

Fig. 6.
MAP OF THE SOUTHERN PART OF THE VALE OF YORK.
The thick lines indicate the position of the York and Escrick Moraines.
(Scale : ⅛-inch to 1 mile).

mond, at Catterick, and Leeming, at Stokesley, and Thirsk, and several places below the range of oolitic rocks between Thirsk and
Pocklington, and commonly in gravel-pits and on the surface of the
country around York."

The second rock, the Carrock Fell gabbro, he records only " near
Lord Darlington's smelt mill at the west pits in Durham."

" The third rock is fully as remarkable and local as either of the
others.   It consists of pebbles of light-coloured mountain-limestone,
united together by red sandstone into a conglomerate provincially
called *brockram*.   This occurs *in situ*, sometimes alternating with red
sandstone, abundantly about Kirkby Stephen, in Westmoreland, as at
Stenkrith Bridge, where the Eden has forced through it a romantic and
beautiful channel.

" I have observed pebbles of this curious rock at Scotton, south-east
of Richmond . . . ."[1]

Translating this in terms of the glacial theory: a glacier passed from
the Lake District, over Stainmore and into the Vale of York.

The ridges we have traced in this chapter, namely, that through
York, Grimston, Holtby and Gate Helmsley; and the other through
Stillingfleet, Escrick, Wheldrake, Sutton upon Derwent, and High
Catton, are the terminal moraines of this glacier.

CHAPTER XIII.

THE YORK AND ESCRICK MORAINES.

The first suggestion that these were the terminal moraines of a great glacier
appears to have been made by Dakyns, though his meaning is not clearly ex-
pressed . . .

P. F. KENDALL, 1922.

Dakyn's thesis can be completely and clearly presented by taking
four short extracts from his paper[1] : —

" A great deal of the drift is as angular as ordinary moraine-matter
might be expected to be; but a great deal of it is also composed of
rounded pebbles, well scratched; and yet these two cannot be separated
from one another; and the rounded and scratched drift has often the
characteristic shape of moraine, whether terminal or lateral.   But rocks
riding on the surface of a glacier, and shed therefrom, will be neither
rounded nor scratched.   The latter kind of drift, then, did not so come.
But rocks sticking in the bottom of a glacier will be both rounded and
scratched, and the more so the further they have travelled."

" Besides the scratched gravels, we have also in certain places mounds
of water-worn gravels arranged in confused heaps, often enclosing hol-

[1]*Phil. Mag.*, vol. ii, 1827, p. 138.
[1]*Q.J.G.S.*, vol. xxviii, 1872, pp. 384, 385 and 386.

lows, known by the name of Kames or Eskers. These kames bear a distinct relation to the valley; they occur at certain parts only of the valley, and were evidently deposited in the bottom of it; they form irregular mounds, sometimes quite blocking up the valley; they consist of stones that have been once scratched, but whose scratches have been worn off, doubtless by the action of the water in which the kames were deposited.''

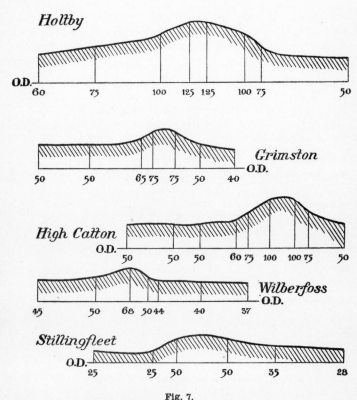

Fig. 7.
PROFILES OF THE YORK AND ESCRICK MORAINES.
(Vertical Scale 8.8 times the Horizontal).

" From the way in which kames pass gradually into scratched gravels, and from the definite position they occupy in the valley, it seems to me probable that in many cases kames are merely the result of moraines deposited in the sea instead of on land."

" In some gravel-pits near York, the structure of these kames is well seen."

Here he figures and describes a section in the gravel-pit at Campleshon Lane, South Bank, a suburb on the south side of the city of York.

Thus a clear distinction is drawn between subaerial moraines, properly so called; and moraines formed under water, here called kames.

Dakyns realised that the York ridge was a moraine; and his insight enabled him to see further—it was a moraine deposited under water.

CHAPTER XIV.

THE YORK AND ESCRICK MORAINES (continued).

The band of sand, gravel, and boulder clay between Escrick and Wheldrake, which has been identified as the outer moraine, though somewhat more conspicuous than that from Fulford to Escrick, is a low, broad rise. Its height is about thirty feet above the adjacent plain; its slopes are gentle and it shows neither the humpiness characteristic of moraines, nor the steep sides of kames.

J. W. GREGORY, January 1922.

The description of the contours of the southern ridge are very misleadingly described by the omission of any reference to the fact that, like its northern fellow, it protrudes through a great mantle of so-called " Warp " clay, and thus both its height and the contour of its flanks are concealed.

Before coming to any decision regarding these remarkable ridges one would have expected a geologist to make himself familiar with their form, constitution, and relation to the adjacent deposits. . . .

P. F. KENDALL, March 1922.

The form of these ridges is indicated by the profiles shown in fig. 7 with a vertical scale 8.8 times the horizontal.

In fig. 8 will be found vertical sections disclosing their constitution; and below is given the thickness of the top boulder clay and overlying sand:—

		Thickness of top Boulder Clay and overlying Sand.
At		Feet.
York Moraine. { Hazelbush, Stockton Common,	... ..	38
Grimston, ...		43
Escrick Moraine. { Gilberson's Farm, ...		36
Stillingfleet, ...		44

The information to be got from these sections may be supplemented by one or two observations.

At Burtonfields, not far from Stamford Bridge, where the two moraines coalesce, there is an extensive gravel-pit, 75 feet above sea-level. It shows boulder clay with an intercalation of bedded sands and gravel, mostly made up of sandstone and limestone pebbles, but with some Keuper Marl together with flint and chalk. A boring put down at a point on a level with the floor of the pit passed through:—

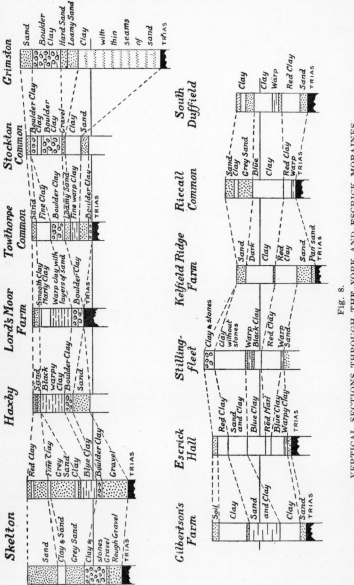

Fig. 8.

VERTICAL SECTIONS THROUGH THE YORK AND ESCRICK MORAINES.
(Vertical Scale : 1 inch to 100 feet).

							Feet.
5.	Yellow clay and gravel,	...	...	...	...	...	3
4.	Blue-black stony clay,	...	...	...	...	...	20
3.	Gravel,	...	...	...	...	...	7
2.	Blue-black stony clay,	...	...	...	...	...	10
1.	Silty clay with small pebbles,	...	...	...	...		4
	Keuper Marl.						

—

44

J. W. Stather has described another section in the Escrick moraine at High Catton, about 1¼ miles south of Burtonfields. Here he saw an exceedingly varied series of current-bedded sand and well-rounded gravel which was " found to consist almost entirely of sandstones and lime-stones from Carboniferous sources. Not a single specimen of a local or a secondary rock was seen in this pit, but several specimens of Shap Granite and other far-travelled igneous rocks were noted. Brockram from the Vale of Eden was also not uncommon.

" On the other hand, near High Catton Grange (one mile N.E. of the above quarry) a small pit was examined, which, in addition to Car-boniferous rocks, contained flints and pebbles of chalk in abundance."[1]

At Sutton upon Derwent, W. V. Vernon Harcourt found the " great diluvial deposit of the vale of York " was 66 feet thick, and rested on gravel of white flint and chalk. Here, and also at Elvington on the opposite bank of the river, this chalk gravel " contains the supply by which the wells are filled; and when it is penetrated into, the water rises more than fifty feet, and blows up a great abundance of the angu-lar fragments of white flint."[2]

Chalk and flint gravel has also been recorded from a depth of about 15 feet below sea-level, at the bottom of a boring put down at the Work-house, Huntington Road, York.[3]

The deepest excavations in the York moraine were those at the Friends' Retreat, York, described by James Edmund Clark in 1881.[4] Boulder clay, 27 feet thick, was found resting on 10 feet of sand; an arrangement evidently much the same as that in the Grimston boring shown in fig. 9. The boulder clay " was in all parts filled with pebbles and boulders, large mounds of which were heaped around. A block of sandstone measured 3 feet by 1½ by 1 foot; its weight, therefore, must have been over a quarter of a ton." Others found were estimated to be nearly a ton in weight.

But on the whole the York moraine does not yield large stones. Most frequently they are less than a foot in size. The rectangular block of encrinital limestone discovered while excavating the swimming bath at Yearsley Bridge, York, estimated to weigh 6½ tons, is unique in this respect.

The York moraine is generally admitted to belong to the period of the Hessle glaciation; pebbles of Cheviot porphyrite are occasionally

[1]Naturalist, 1913, p. 320.
[2]Phil. Mag., vol. vi, 1829, p. 225.
[3]Proc. Yorks. Phil. Soc., 1932, p. 1.
[4]Proc. Yorks. Geol. Soc., vol. vii, 1881, p. 421.

found among the stones; but, as an indication of its age its freshness
is the main criterion.

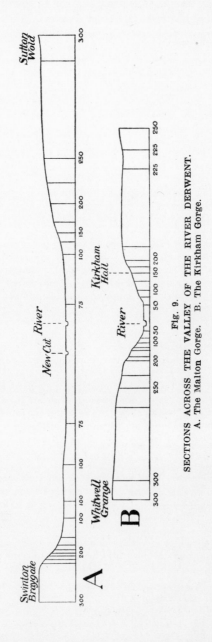

Fig. 9.

SECTIONS ACROSS THE VALLEY OF THE RIVER DERWENT.
A. The Malton Gorge.   B. The Kirkham Gorge.

Regarding the relation of the moraine to adjacent deposits, it is at once evident on inspecting the vertical sections (fig. 9) that north-east of York warp clay rests upon the boulder clay; while at Skelton, to the north-west, we find a corresponding development of sand, indicative of deltaic conditions; and the boulder clay is lost beneath a total thickness of 75 feet of later deposits.

Even so, it remains true that the moraines are indeed mere " rises," low in proportion to their breadth, with gently sloping sides proclaiming their subaqueous origin. Nor can we claim for them the full thickness of the deposits between the rock floor and the present surface. The moraine accounts for only the upper third of the deposits in the Grimston boring; and it is thus open to doubt whether the deposits beneath the boulder clay in the other borings are part of the moraine.   According to A. Raistrick[5] they belong to the age of the Upper Purple glaciation of the eastern Pennine slope.

This much is certain : a glacier moving down the Vale of York could not bring chalk and flint gravel to Elvington.

CHAPTER XV.

THE VALE OF PICKERING AND THE VALLEY OF THE DERWENT.

The level vale of Pickering, partly formed upon a surface of Boulder-clay, may be regarded as a large Preglacial vale, or sea-loch, which became blocked during the Glacial depression by drift at its eastern end.   Through this drift short streams have since cut their way to the sea, to which, in earlier times, the Derwent had probably flowed by a short and rapid course, accompanied, most likely, by the Seven, Rye, and other western waters, which now descend to the Humber through the gorge at Malton.

JOHN PHILLIPS, 1868.

This " large Preglacial vale, or sea-loch," is terminated at its western end by a buried cliff, corresponding to that running south-west from Sewerby into Holderness.   From Malton the cliff may be traced northward through Ryton, and thence in the direction of Thornton Dale. At Great Habton, the superficial deposits are only 10 feet thick, resting on the Kimeridge Clay at 70 feet O.D.; and at Parnham House, 1¼ miles to the east, the rock floor is 9 feet above the sea; but in a boring put down at Howe about 2 miles further to the east, 97 feet of superficial deposits were passed through before the floor was reached at −30 feet O.D.

Instead of boulder clays resting on this floor, as in Holderness, we find, at the west end, clays of the type that would be deposited in a lake.

[5]*Proc. Yorks. Geol. Soc.*, vol. xxii, 1934, p. 202.

It is quite possible the ice of the Basement and Purple Clay periods may have laid down boulder clays far into the interior of the loch; but there is now no trace of them.

If the ice of the Basement Clay period reached as far as Scarborough and Filey, as it probably did, the conversion of the sea-loch into a lake must have taken place then; but at present it is impossible to say whether this blockage was permanent.   A time came, however, when the east end was effectively stopped up, and the lake overflowed through " the gorge at Malton."

It is interesting to note that most accounts of this phenomenon written since the time of Phillips direct attention exclusively to the gorge at Kirkham. But on inspection of any contour-map of the district it will be seen that a ridge running from Appleton-le-Street to Langton Wold, and cut through by the River Derwent, just below Malton, calls for consideration first.

Fox-Strangeways' account[1] takes this into consideration.   " The gorge below Malton," he says, " seems to have been formed in a similar manner to the Forge Valley [*i.e.*, as a lake-overflow], but with this difference that an older stream course probably existed on the same site.   This stream, from the northerly dip of the beds here, would originally flow north into the Vale of Pickering, as is the case with the Wath Beck near Hovingham and other streams in these hills; but from the limited area of drainage it would not have been any larger than these streams."

A section across the Malton gorge is shown in fig. 9*a*. Its mature features, and the fact that the rock floor at Norton is 20 feet below sea-level, lend support to the idea that the Appleton-Langton Wold ridge was already severed before the gorge began to serve as a lake overflow channel. We may take this to be true also of the ridge which slopes eastward from Hutton Hill to Eddlethorpe Grange.

The height at which the cutting of the Kirkham gorge commenced has been variously estimated at between 200 and 250 feet O.D. From the section shown in fig. 9*b* it would appear that it began at about 225 feet. But there is ground between Westow and Gally Gap below this level, and only a few feet above 200 feet O.D. If the filling in of the gaps which the Derwent has cut through these ridges is all that is necessary to restore the topography to its original state, it is clear the southward overflow from Lake Pickering would be to the east of the present river.

Granted the existence of a river, no bigger than Wath Beck, flowing into the Vale of Pickering at that early period, it may be that the whole channel from Malton to Stamford Bridge is due to river capture, as between this ancient stream and another flowing into the Vale of York.

We know no more about the origin of the Derwent valley than of that other between Kipling Cotes and Market Weighton, referred to in a previous chapter.

[1] *Jurassic Rocks of Britain*, vol. i, 1892, p. 423.

The condition of the Derwent valley at the time the Hessle glaciation was at a maximum is, however, fairly clear. When the ice reached
the position marked out by the Escrick moraine, it lay across the valley
of the Derwent. This obstruction caused the river to rise and form a
lake, the traces of which can be seen, for example, in the Spittle Beck
valley, between Whitwell and Barton le Willows. Here brick-clay occurs
up to a height of nearly 100 feet O.D., as it does in the Vale of Pickering. The Derwent valley above Stamford Bridge, and the Vale of
Pickering must then have been one level sheet of water. The Kirkham
gorge must already have been cut down below 100 feet O.D.

CHAPTER XVI.

THE WESTERN LAKES.

*In my former paper I briefly noticed the great accumulation of coarse gravel
on the plains which skirt the western moors of Yorkshire. Had this gravel been
formed by a number of lakes which were once pent up among the mountains,
and afterwards burst their way into the lower regions of the district, we might
expect to find traces of such lakes in the interior of the moorlands, and distinct
heaps of gravel marking the devastations produced by the discharge of the
successive lakes into the plain of the new red sandstone.*

ADAM SEDGWICK, 1825.

We have seen how the ice of the Hessle glaciation, when it lay
in the position marked by the Escrick moraine, blocked up the drainage of the River Derwent and formed a lake. Is there any evidence of
similar lake-formation at the west end of the moraine?

First, let us trace the moraine from Escrick, westward. At Stillingfleet it is cut through by the River Ouse; but on the opposite bank it
is seen forming the high ground between Nun Appleton and Bolton
Percy. At Tadcaster the position of the ice-edge is very clearly marked
by an "in-and-out" channel, formed by the drainage water flowing
through it from the north. This channel has cut off the hill just north
of the Cemetery from the high ground to the west; the bottom of it, at
its highest point, stands at 70 feet O.D.

The lake, whose waters overflowed through this channel, is represented to-day by a deposit of sand and laminated clay well seen in a
pit at Firgreen Bridge, near Clifford. The top of the pit is at a height
of 75 feet above sea-level. The section is as follows:—

	Feet.
Red loamy sand, ...	2 - 2½
Yellow current-bedded sand, gravelly in places, ...	4
Laminated clay, ...	2
Yellow sand with clayey seams, ...	6

The next evidence of lake-formation is met in the valley of the Nidd. Here the position of the ice-edge corresponding with the Escrick moraine is marked by a quadrant-shaped dry valley running from North Deighton to Kirk Deighton. The cutting of this channel began at a height of about 135 feet O.D., when the normal course of the River Nidd was blocked by ice lying across it between Little Ribston and Ribston Park. The lake so formed has left traces of its existence in the form of brick-clay, which can be seen in Goldsborough Park and followed to a height of 110 feet above sea-level, at Flaxby Covert, close to Allerton Park.

The York moraine continues westward from that city, through Bilbrough, Healaugh, Bilton and Bickerton; it forms a well-marked ridge at Cowthorpe, and thence turns north through Hunsingore to Allerton Park. At Grafton, 3 miles further north, it is being very extensively worked, and the boulder clay, with stones of large size, is well exposed. This boulder clay can be followed to Boroughbridge, where it can be seen in the road-side opposite the Cemetery at 75 feet O.D. The well in St James' Square is wholly in this boulder clay, which proved to be 28 feet thick, resting directly on the New Red Sandstone. Although the ground half a mile to the west of the Cemetery is at the same height, it consists of laminated clay, extensive sections of which can be seen at the Roecliffe Brick and Tile Works. This brick clay is also exposed at the Park Hill Pottery, near Littlethorpe. The waters of the River Ure have clearly been impounded in the same way as those of the Nidd.

The end of the Hessle glacier in the Vale of York is thus symmetrical about its longitudinal axis, both as regards the shape of the moraine and the arrangement of the lateral lakes. Nor are these the only symmetrical features; for at Whitwell Hill and Hutton Hill,[1] beyond the eastern border of the moraine, there is a driftless area; and corresponding with this, outside the western border, we find the village of Goldsborough stands upon a hill of Magnesian Limestone, without any covering of drift.

CHAPTER XVII.

SOUTH OF THE MORAINES.

. . . a flat and tame district, where sections are few and far between.
H. F. PARSONS, 1877.

At the end of Chapter X the course of the Hessle ice-edge was traced from Craike Hill to Kipling Cotes, at which point the drainage waters

---

[1] During recent road-widening work on Hutton Hill the Estuarine Sandstone was seen without any drift whatever on top.

passed into the Vale of York through the valley leading to Market Weighton.

The position of the ice-front of this period is well-marked in the estuary of the Humber. Transverse sections through the moraine are to be seen at Red Cliff, near North Ferriby; and at South Ferriby Cliff on the Lincolnshire side of the river.[1]

At the top of these sections, there is boulder clay, agreeing in character with that of Hessle; this rests on boulder clay of an earlier type, which may be *in situ*, but more probably has been pushed forward into its present position by the advance of the Hessle ice. Between the two boulder clays, pockets of laminated clay are occasionally seen.

The water-level in the Vale of York at the time the Humber was thus stopped up can be determined within narrow limits. The upper limit is fixed by the height of the " in-and-out " channel at Tadcaster, which, as we have seen, stands at 70 feet O.D.

The deposits at the west end of the Kipling Cotes channel yield further evidence on this point. A boring put down at Goodmanham Spring, half way along this valley, passed through :—

		Feet.
Soil,	... ...	1
Gravel,	... ...	19
Chalk gravel,	... ...	30
Chalk,	... ...	—

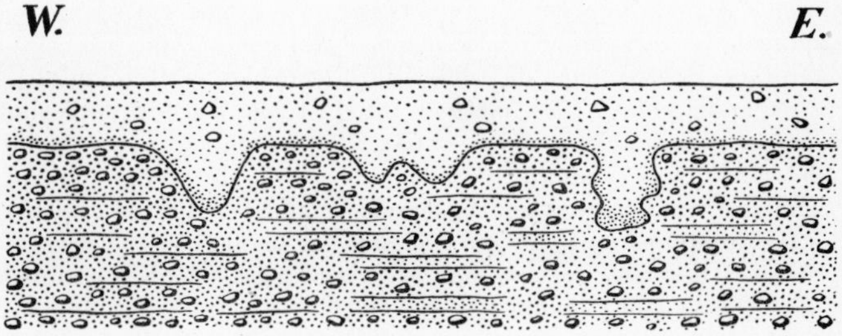

W.   **E.**

Fig. 10.
SECTION IN PIT AT SANDFIELD HOUSE, MARKET WEIGHTON.
Showing brown loamy sand resting on an eroded surface of flint and chalk gravel.

At the outlet of the valley, brown sand takes the place of the upper gravel in this boring. This sand can be seen in a pit behind Sandfield House, Market Weighton. The top of the pit is at 65 feet O.D. The section here is shown in fig. 10. The gravel at the bottom consists mostly of flint and chalk. No far-travelled erratics have so far been found in it. Its upper surface is eroded, and the pockets are lined with an inch or two of clay, passing rapidly into brown loamy sand.

[1]These sections were described in 1899 by J. W. Stather in *Proc. Yorks. Geol. Soc.*, vol. xiii, p. 210. A more recent account, by W. S. Bisat, will be found in *Trans. Hull Geol. Soc.*, vol. vii, 1930-1931, p. 83.

Pebbles occur sparingly in this top sand, and are mostly white flints: but a rhomb-porphyry and two Cheviot porphyrites have been found in it.   There are no rhombohedral carbonates in this sand, and zircon is more abundant than garnet.   The streaks of horizontally-bedded sand which occur here and there in the lower gravel contain carbonates, and the zircon-garnet ratio is reversed.   The lower deposits are thus markedly different from the upper.

The same arrangement of beds can be seen at other places further south; but in every case the top sand rests on an eroded surface of gravel.   Thus near South Cave it lies upon gravel containing innumerable specimens of *Gryphaea*, derived from the Lias; with some flint.

An account of such gravels, written by Vernon Harcourt in 1826, after journeying with Phillips as far as Cave, is of two-fold interest. The passage contains a perfect record of field observations, and a good description of a neat and convenient chemical test.

" It only remains to add, that on our return we met with the red marle again a mile to the west of Shipton, and that at Holme, we observed the gravel to consist of the same fragments of sandstone and grit, mountain lime and slate, as in other parts of the Vale of York, but that at every point where we met with gravel near the chalk hills, it consisted of materials brought from a very short distance; and though the soft chalk pebbles were rounded, the gryphites and flints were very little rubbed.   In one of these beds of gravel we observed a seam which bore a remarkably black and sooty appearance; I examined the powder which occasioned this colour, and which formed a mamillary incrustation on some of the pebbles, and found it to be oxide of manganese.   The method which I employ for detecting the presence of manganese is very simple.   To the end of a platina wire I attach a little subcarbonate of soda and a particle of the substance to be examined, and hold it in the exterior flame of a candle either just above the luminous point, or on one side; if manganese be present, the melted bead becomes, on cooling, of a turquoise colour; on immersing it into the visible flame it loses this colour, and resumes it again when re-exposed to that portion of the flame which emits little light, and where the combustion is perfect."[2]

Gravel coated with oxide of manganese was to be seen recently in a pit at Thorpe-le-Street, between Market Weighton and Pocklington, but is no longer worked.

The fact noted by Vernon Harcourt, that wherever we meet with gravel near the chalk hills, it consists of materials brought from a very short distance, is certainly remarkable; and one which can easily be verified.   Thus at Thorpe-le-Street, the gravel contains much Triassic sandstone, whereas at Market Weighton there is none.   At South Cave the gravel is full of *Gryphaea* shells; while further south, as at Brantingham Grange, it is almost entirely made up of Millepore Oolite, with few pebbles of Liassic, and none of Triassic origin.

---

[2] *Annals of Phil.*, vol. xi, 1826, p. 435.

Beds of sand and gravel, agreeing with those already described in constitution and height above sea-level, are also found on the west side of the Vale of York.   Fig. 11 shows the section visible in a pit near the gas-works at Boston Spa, near Tadcaster.   The coarse gravel at the bottom is mostly of Carboniferous origin, but a few pebbles of red marl and one of green volcanic ash have been found in it.   Above this comes a layer of fine current-bedded sand, 14 inches thick, followed by finer gravel of the same composition as that below.   The upper surface of the top gravel is pockety and overlain by red loam with small pebbles, as at Market Weighton.

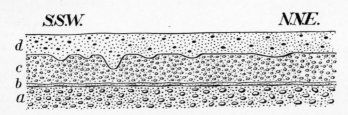

S.S.W.   **N.N.E.**

Fig. 11.

SECTION IN PIT AT BOSTON SPA.

a. Coarse gravel, mostly of Carboniferous rocks.   *b.* Fine current-bedded sand.
c. Gravel, finer than that below, but similar in composition.   The upper surface
is pockety.   *d.* Red loam with small pebbles.

On the reopening of the Humber gap, at the decline of the Hessle glaciation, the outflowing waters cut their way down to at least 24 feet O.D.   This can be inferred from the section near North Ferriby described and figured by W. S. Bisat.[3]   Here a dark brown clayey subsoil with angular flints and some small angular chalk pebbles rests upon an eroded surface of angular chalk and flint gravel.   Laminated clay and boulder clay lie beneath the gravel.   Among the stones in the boulder clay, chalk and flint predominate, but basalt, Mountain Limestone, Magnesian Limestone, Cheviot porphyrite, and various Oolitic rocks also occur.

The sequence of brown sandy loam upon an eroded surface of gravel is obviously the same as that in the other sections described in this chapter.

[3]*Trans. Hull Geol. Soc.*, vol. vi, 1922, p. 238.

CHAPTER XVIII.

THE BASE OF THE HESSLE CLAY.

It seems, therefore, that not only has the sea-level altered, but many of the valleys in the Boulder Clay have been cut since the period of the Raised Beaches.

CLEMENT REID, 1885.

The sequence of the glacial deposits of Holderness, as established by Wood and Rome, has been tabulated in Chapter IV. Gravel underlies the Hessle Clay, and beneath the gravel comes the Purple Clay. Our next concern is therefore to trace the junction of the Purple and Hessle clays from Holderness into the Vale of York. We may embark upon the attempt at Hull.

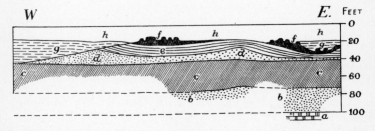

Fig. 12.

SECTION CONSTRUCTED FROM BORINGS AT THE HULL DOCKS
(after Wood and Rome).

a. Chalk.   *b.* Sand with chalk-rubble.   *c.* The Purple Clay.   *d.* The Hessle Sand.
e. The Hessle Clay.   *f.* Peat-bed with the stools of trees *in situ.*   *g.* Silt with
Tellina solidula, Scrobicularia piperata, Cardium edule, etc.   *h.* Salt water.
Length of Section about one mile; vertical scale about eleven times the horizontal.
The zero line is the High Water Mark.

A series of twenty-nine borings along the river-front, preliminary to dock-excavations at this place, was discussed and figured by Wood and Rome in their paper of 1868. The horizontal section derived from the borings is shown in fig. 12. The trace of the Purple Clay is seen to be horizontal, and is at a depth of 40 feet below high-water mark, or about 30 feet below O.D. A bed of sand rests upon the clay, and above it lies the Hessle Clay. The uppermost deposit is a peat bed. That these clays were rightly identified by Wood and Rome as the Purple and Hessle clays is born out by W. H. Crofts' observations[1]

[1]*Trans. Hull Geol. Soc.,* vol. v, 1903, p. 57.

made during more recent dock-excavations.   He says: " The lower
bed may possibly be what is known as the ' Purple ' Clay containing a
large number of striated Chalk boulders, Basalt, Cheviot Porphyrites,
Carboniferous Limestone, etc., but no Scandinavian rocks were seen."
The upper boulder clay " generally resembled the so-called ' Hessle
Clay,' containing many Chalk Boulders and having ashey coloured
joints."

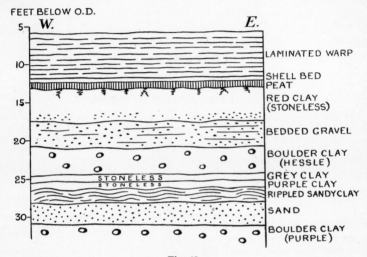

Fig. 13.
SECTION SEEN IN THE ALEXANDRA DOCK EXTENSION, HULL
(after W. H. Crofts).

In the excavations described by Crofts (fig. 13), the top of the
Purple Boulder Clay is at about − 30 feet O.D., and the base of the
Hessle Clay at − 25 feet O.D. approximately.

A sample of boulder clay dredged up from a submerged bank a
little to the east of the mouth of the River Hull, has been described
by Sheppard.[2]   It contained Carboniferous Limestone, Liassic and
Oolitic fragments and fossils, chalk, basalts, red granites, etc.   " It is
apparent that the Bank consists of the Middle [i.e., Purple] Boulder
Clay."

At the type locality, the Hessle Clay overlies gravel resting, by a
coincidence, as we have seen, upon the marine peneplain.   This gravel
is not, however, the equivalent of the Sewerby gravel.

The Hull dock-excavations, then, show that at the time the Hessle
Clay was laid down the land was not far removed from its present level
—perhaps about 20 feet higher.

In the North Ferriby section, described by Bisat, the top of the
Purple Boulder Clay is at about 20 feet above sea-level.   This is the

2The Naturalist, 1913, p. 87.

most westerly point in the Humber gap to which the Purple Clay has been traced with any aproach to continuity.   No boulder clay was passed through in a boring put down at Brough, three miles west of North Ferriby; or in another on Read's Island.   Here we lose sight of all direct evidence of the Purple Boulder Clay glaciation.

CHAPTER XIX.

HOLM UPON SPALDING MOOR.

At this place . . . the Keuper rises into a picturesque little hill, 150 feet in height, steep on three sides, but somewhat shelving to the south. The summit of the hill is capped with gravel about 10 feet thick, very similar to that at Heck, with no fragments of the local rock; on the slopes of the hill the red and green Marls are exposed, only covered with a few scattered pebbles; but on the east side a low gravelly ridge stretches away nearly half a mile from the hill, the gravel being composed in great part of flat water-worn fragments of green marly sandstone derived from the Keuper.

H. F. PARSONS, 1877.

A bed of gravel on the top of an isolated hill 150 feet above the sea is an odd thing; but when the composition of the gravel is taken into account, it becomes remarkable.

The deposit is about 10 feet thick, as Parsons has recorded, and rests upon the Keuper Marl.   The lowest part, for the thickness of about a foot, consists of sand; but above that it is almost entirely gravel, with occasional seams of sand.

The gravel is interesting as much for what it does not contain as for what it does.   It does not contain any material derived from the Trias; it consists almost wholly of Carboniferous rocks.   Now it is obvious that a stream flowing from the Pennines, across Triassic rocks to Holme, would pick up and there deposit gravel containing fragments of such rocks.   But when the gravel which we actually find there is examined, none are found.   Clearly, therefore, the waters did not run over an outcrop of the Trias.   The outcrop was protected from erosion; other deposits must have lain upon it; and for this to be so, the surface of the outcrop between the Pennines and Holme must have been lower than 150 feet O.D.

Flints occur sparingly in the gravel.   Rocks foreign to the district are extremely rare; they are nearly all of sedimentary types, including yellow flint.   An orthoclase-porphyry has been found, but this does not occur with a greater frequency than about 1 in 4000.[1]

[1] A more detailed account of this deposit will be found in *Q.J.G.S.*, vol. xc, 1934, p. 141.

The gravel at the foot of the hill is excellently exposed in a pit at the north-east corner. The face of the pit is about 80 yards long and 20 feet high. Bold lines of current-bedding make this a most imposing

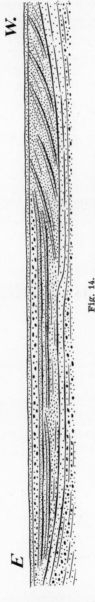

Fig. 14.

SECTION IN PIT AT THE FOOT OF CHURCH HILL, HOLME, at 50 feet O.D.
Length of Section about 80 yards; height 20 feet.

section (fig. 14), but from top to bottom the composition of the gravel is the same. It consists, as Parsons observed, very largely of **Keuper marl**; but there is a very small proportion of yellow sandstone, probably of Jurassic origin; and pebbles of Carboniferous Limestone and breccia are occasionally to be found. White and yellow flints occur, as in the gravel at the top of the hill, but here at the bottom red flints are found in addition.

On the west side, the foot of the hill is buried in sand. The well at the Blacksmith's Arms passed through 15 feet of it before entering the Marl.

The gravel of Keuper Marl is unlike any other in the district, and unfortunately, it is at present impossible to determine its age; though as a " monolithic " deposit, it may be classed with the gravel of **Mille-pore Oolite** at Brantingham Grange.

On the top of it there is no trace whatever of the brown sand of Market Weighton; so it cannot safely be concluded that it is of the same age as the chalk and flint gravel. Nor do the exposures available at the present time enable us to determine the relation between the Keuper gravel and that consisting of sandstone, grit, and Carboniferous Limestone noticed by Vernon Harcourt on his return journey from Cave in 1826.

CHAPTER XX.

BRAYTON BARFF AND THE HIGH-LEVEL DEPOSITS ON THE EAST SIDE OF THE VALE OF YORK.

At a higher level, nearer Elloughton, is a gravel with rounded boulders of Carboniferous Sandstone and Millstone Grit.

H. F. PARSONS, 1877.

Another small isolated hill is that of Brayton Barff, 2½ miles west-south-west of Selby. This rises to a height of 160 feet above sea-level. To-day, only one of the deposits forming the summit is open for examination; but in 1915, when a reservoir was being constructed for the supply of water to Selby, the deposits on the top of the hill were fully exposed. They were about 12 feet thick, and according to a contemporary account published by T. Sheppard[1] the general succession was : —

    3. White marl with decayed vegetable matter.
    2. Very fine clay.
    1. Gravel.
    0. Bunter Sandstone.

[1] *The Naturalist*, 1915, p. 290.

The fine clay may still be seen on the south side of the summit.

Specimens of the following rocks were obtained from the gravel: Cheviot porphyrite, hornblende-rock from the Lake District, Carboniferous sandstone (common), Millstone Grit, Carboniferous Limestone and chert (common), and white quartz.

It will be seen that these deposits capping the hills are as diverse in character as those on the plain at their feet; and it is clear they are but the remnants of a sheet that must once have spread over a considerable area. It becomes of interest, therefore, to search for traces of this sheet along the slopes of the Wolds and the Pennines. The height of ·these deposits above both the plain and the Escrick moraine is in itself sufficient to prove that they are older than the Hessle glaciation; and I do not know of any remains of this sheet of pebbles north of the Escrick moraine. We will therefore begin at Bishop Wilton and work southward.

Bishop Wilton stands at the mouth of a considerable valley known as Worsen Dale, now occupied by the little Bishop Wilton Beck. This valley rises close to Garrowby Hill Top, and after cutting its way through the Chalk, Red Chalk, Lias, Rhaetic and Keuper, dies out at about 200 feet O.D. Evidently at the period when the stream was in full activity it approached the limit of its course at approximately this level.

The same is true of the magnificent Millington Dale, which in its upper reaches exhibits to perfection the bold sculpturing characteristic of the dry valleys of the chalk Wolds. It maintains this aspect as far as Millington Springs; here Millington Beck now rises, and a softening of the features sets in, and increases rapidly below the village of Millington; at a little below 200 feet a comparatively flat tract is reached.

In these two cases the existence of a local base-level is a matter of inference; but south of Pocklington the evidence is of a more material kind.

Between Pocklington and Burnby the surface rises fairly rapidly until a slightly dissected flat is reached at a height of 180 feet O.D. Gravel is here exposed in a little pit at Throstle Wood. It consists mostly of chalk with very little flint; but pebbles of Jurassic rocks are fairly plentiful and include fragments of the Passage Beds of the Middle Oolites, which must have come from some northerly source. Chert and quartz pebbles are among the rare constituents.

Near Market Weighton the evidence is somewhat similar to that at Bishop Wilton and Millington. A dry tributary valley joins the Kipling Cotes-Market Weighton channel on its north side and overhangs it at a height of 170 feet above sea-level. This hanging valley has been noted by Kendall and Wroot.[2]

Continuing southward, gravel occurs at Sancton between 160 and 200 feet O.D., but is not now well exposed. Sand covers the Lias at the top of Cliff Hill, overlooking North Cliff; while at Newbald, to the east

[2]Kendall, P. F., and H. E. Wroot. *The Geology of Yorkshire*, 1924, p. 812.

of this place, boulders of " Red Granite " and " Hard Limestone " have been recorded by T. Tate.[3]

At South -Cave we come upon remarkable indications of glacial action, at about 150 feet above sea-level. Here occurs a great displaced mass of Millepore Oolite. Between it and the Millepore Oolite *in situ*, there is interposed a drift deposit ranging up to 6 feet in thickness. It is a gritty chalk-wash consisting mostly of fragments of flint and chalk with occasional pieces of Red Chalk and Millepore limestone. A few erratics found in it have been identified by P. F. Kendall as quartz-porphyry, sheared granite, fine-grained felsite with tourmaline, Cheviot porphyrite and red sandstone.   At the top of the drift, immediately below the displaced oolite there are usually a few inches of dark blue or blackish clay.

The displacement of the limestone can only be explained by supposing it to have been " carried over the newer deposits by some transporting agency, presumably glacial."[4]

Before going further south in search of high-level gravels, we may pause here to enquire whether there are signs of disturbance in any other deposits in the neighbourhood.

A pit one mile west of South Cave village shows the *Gryphaea* gravel, mentioned in the last chapter, with the usual brown sand overlying it. The top sand is undisturbed, but the gravel beneath dips, in places, at a high angle to the north-west and also to the north-east. Near Brough, a little over two miles south of Cave, in some gravel pits, near the Cave Road, Parsons has recorded " a gravel composed of angular fragments of local rocks, mostly oolite and lias, in highly inclined beds, resting unconformably upon horizontal strata of sand and laminated clay."[5]

A description of the deposits on the top of the Mill Hill, near Elloughton, mentioned by Parsons in 1877, will complete our survey of high-level deposits on the east side of the Vale of York.

The beds capping this hill were described by Lamplugh[6] in 1887, and later by Sheppard.[7]

The section given by Sheppard is as follows : —

		Feet.
3.	Soil, ...	about 1
2.	Current-bedded gravel, chiefly local flint and chalk, ...	about 6
1.	Very tough earthy sand and gravel, chiefly Coal Measures sandstones, ...	about 2

[3] *The Naturalist*, 1894, p. 297.

[4] This remarkable section has been described by J. W. Stather in *Proc. Yorks. Geol. Soc.*, vol. xix, 1921-1922, p. 395; from which account the above particulars have been taken.

[5] *Proc. Yorks. Geol. Soc.*, vol. vi, 1879, p. 220, footnote.

[6] *Proc. Yorks. Geol. Soc.*, vol. ix, 1887, p. 407.

[7] *Ibid.*, vol. xiii, 1896, p. 221.

These rest upon the Estuarine Oolites.

The lower gravel, which consists chiefly of Coal Measures sandstones, has yielded remains of the following mammalia:—*Elephas primigenius, E. antiquus, Bos primigenius, Bison priscus* (?), *Cervus elaphus, C.* sp., *Equus caballus.*

At the bottom of it Sheppard observed a large boulder of the Whin Sill basalt, standing on end; and also a specimen of augite-syenite.

The upper gravel is composed mostly of local flint and chalk, with red chalk, oolite sandstone and other local rocks; together with a few well-worn erratics of felstone, and quartzite. It contains also rolled lumps of clay, and thin seams of clay and carbonaceous matter.

Lamplugh put forward the following explanation of the deposits on Mill Hill: " The non-occurrence of marine shells suggests fluviatile conditions, and it is possible that the beds have accumulated in fresh water when the drainage of the Lower Humber was encumbered and the waters dammed back by ice. The sudden withdrawal of this icy barrier might explain the rather curious preservation of these incoherent gravels on the crest of an isolated hill with bare slopes, for under such conditions the hill might emerge as an island and the deposits on its summit be preserved while its slopes were undergoing torrential denudation."

CHAPTER XXI.

THE HIGH-LEVEL DEPOSITS ON THE WEST SIDE OF THE VALE OF YORK.

Dr Milligan and Mr Bottomley have satisfied me that at least one of three specimens of Gryphaea, found by them at Keighley, was obtained from the blue clay, and they believe that the other two had come out of the blue clay or overlying drift.

D. MACKINTOSH, 1870.

Successive glaciations and intervening periods of erosion have produced a more varied series of deposits on the west side of the Vale of York than any so far discovered on the east; and have rendered the determination of their relationship proportionately more difficult. We shall now, therefore, merely describe the deposits as they are met with in going from north to south; and leave the discussion of them till a later chapter.

The neighbourhood of Bramham, 3½ miles west of Tadcaster, is comparatively driftless; old clay pits at 160 feet and an old sand pit at 150 feet O.D., which might have yielded useful information, are now grassed over. But sands and gravels are found on the top of Wingate Hill, which rises 200 feet above sea-level, about 1½ miles south-west of Tadcaster. The section here (fig. 15), is about 70 yards long and 20 feet

high.   At the bottom of the south-western end coarse gravel passes
upward into fine sharp sand, red loam, and, finally, red laminated clay
two inches thick.   Above this are two mounds of fine sand nine feet

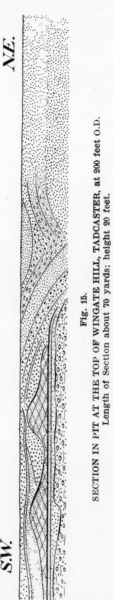

Fig. 15.

SECTION IN PIT AT THE TOP OF WINGATE HILL, TADCASTER, at 200 feet O.D.
Length of Section about 70 yards; height 20 feet.

high showing beautiful current-bedding on a minute scale and having here and there streaks of coal or lignite; these are buried in gravel and coarse sand succeeded by eight inches of red sandy loam thinning out north-eastward. On top of all is more coarse gravel four feet thick.

In the middle of the section the beds exhibit a curious V-shaped structure, and beyond this in a north-easterly direction the gravel beds for the most part thin out, fine sharp yellow sand being the main constituent throughout the whole height of the section.

The sands are of the Carboniferous type and, on flotation in carbon tetrachloride, often yield a considerable amount of woody matter in the form of small grains. The gravels consist almost wholly of Carboniferous sandstone, a little black Carboniferous Limestone and some Magnesian Limestone. W. G. Fearnsides found here a greywacke pebble, and this is the only non-local rock so far discovered.

Near Hazelwood Castle, three miles south-west of Tadcaster, there is brick-clay at 175 feet, possibly related to that, already mentioned, near Bramham.

D. Mackintosh[1] has described and figured a section at a place, between 200 and 250 feet above the sea, on the Bramham-Aberford road. Here the Magnesian Limestone was seen overlaid by patches of dark clay and sand. Above this came gravel, consisting of well-rounded pebbles and boulders in a sandy matrix, about 10 feet in thickness. Over all lay reddish clay, with rounded and subangular stones up to 2 feet in diameter, consisting of sandstone, Millstone Grit, Carboniferous Limestone, chert, and local Permian fragments.

At Whin Moor, which is about 400 feet above the sea, and lies 5 miles west of Aberford and 4 miles north-east of Leeds, a bore hole went through 114 feet of stony clay in which " shells like cockle shells, brittle and readily falling to powder " are said to have been found. This clay is of the kind which forms great masses north of Leeds. It is a " stiff blue clay containing rounded and angular stones, among which the following have been noticed: millstone grit and other carboniferous sandstones, hard shale occasionally, chert with and without encrinital stems, trap, flesh-coloured granite, chalk, and magnesian limestone."[2]

Mackintosh[3] described and figured a section exposed in 1870 in excavations for the Headingley waterworks. The succession was:—

3. Yellowish-blue and variegated clay,[4] with many boulders of sandstone, millstone grit, etc., reaching a diameter of at least 5 feet.
2. Metalliferous laminated sand, traversed by splashy seams of purple loam.
1. Purplish-blue clay with a few boulders, very compact except where it was often to be seen passing into sand. It reaches a thickness of at least 26 feet.

[1] *Proc. Yorks. Geol. Soc.*, vol. v, 1870, p. 155.
[2] Green, A. H., and R. Russell, *Geology of the Yorkshire Coalfield*, 1878, p. 779.
[3] Mackintosh, *loc. cit.*, p. 156.
[4] It has been shown conclusively by A. Jowett and H. B. Muff that the yellowish clay of this district is merely the oxidised top of the blue clay. See page 201 of their exhaustive account of the Glaciation of the Bradford and Keighley District, *Proc. Yorks. Geol. Soc.*, vol. xv, 1904, p. 193.

The gravels at Rothwell Haigh and Oulton, 5 miles south-east of
Leeds, have been described by several writers.[5]

They stand at between 150 and 275 feet above sea-level, but mostly
above 200 feet; and consist of about 90 per cent. of Coal Measure sandstone pebbles; the rest being Millstone Grit, ironstone nodules, large
quartz pebbles, and occasionally Carboniferous Limestone. A few
Silurian or Ordovician rocks, and one or two doubtful igneous specimens
have also been recorded.

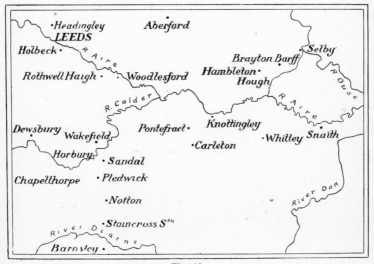

Fig. 16.
MAP OF THE DISTRICT SOUTH-EAST OF LEEDS.
(Scale : ⅛-inch to 1 mile).

Hawkesworth gives the following section in the Rothwell Haigh
deposit, as seen in the large pit nearly opposite the John o' Gaunt Inn,
between 200 and 225 feet above sea-level :—

	Feet.
Very coarse gravel or shingle, ...	2 to 3
Sand, ...	about 15
Very coarse gravel, ...	10 to 12
Sand, ...	about 1
Rough gravel, with large boulders, thickness not known	

A few lenticular masses of clay occur in the sand. When seen by me
in 1933 an impersistent seam of sand black with woody matter was
noticed 10 feet below the surface at the east end of the pit; traces of the
same were also seen at the west end.

Gilligan records the presence of boulder clay at the top of the section,
overlying laminated clay with " race " (concretions of carbonate of

[5] Green and Russell, *op. cit.*, p. 783; E. Hawkesworth, *Proc. Yorks. Geol. Soc.*,
vol. xv, 1905, p. 456; A. Gilligan, *ibid.*, vol. xix, 1918, p. 255.

lime). At the east end, the boulder clay cuts out the laminated clay
and rests directly on the sand. The stones in the boulder clay are
usually Carboniferous Limestone or fine-grained sandstone. According
to P. F. Kendall, some of the limestone is of a type to be matched only
by that near Richmond.

Blocks of Magnesian Limestone, up to 12 x 10 x 7 inches were found
in the laminated clay. None had so far been noted in the boulder clay
above or in the sands and gravels below.

Green and Russell believed these Rothwell gravels to be " river
gravels of considerable antiquity." Gilligan regards them as having
been deposited in a lake formed by the damming-up of the waters of
the Aire by a glacier moving down the Vale of York.

The record,[6] preserved by J. W. Davis, of a well sunk in Dewsbury
is of great value in showing the existence of two distinctly different
layers of boulders : —

		Feet.
4.	Earth and sandy sub-soil, ...	7½
3.	Boulders, consisting principally of sandstone, gradually merging into	24
2.	Boulders nearly all of crystalline rocks, ...	6
1.	Clay, with sand and boulders, ...	5
0.	White rock, of Carboniferous formation.	

The stones in the upper boulder bed consisted of sandstone and other
local rocks, with a slight intermixture of erratics which became more
numerous in the lower part; until, in the lower boulder bed " they
predominate to such an extent that the local rocks are as rarely found
as the crystalline ones were in the upper part of the series."

Unfortunately, the crystalline rocks are not described, but from
the context it would appear they were of Lake District types.

From Dewsbury we pass south-eastward to Horbury, about 2½ miles
south-west of Wakefield. In an excavation for the pier of a bridge
here over the River Calder, W. G. Fearnsides[7] found boulders of Shap
granite, brockram, rhomb-porphyry, and brown flint.

The drift in the village of Horbury has been described by D. A.
Wray.[8] Immediately west of the church, at a height of about 250 feet
above sea-level, or 160 feet above the level of the river, there was found
a sub-soil of clayey gravel, 4 to 6 feet thick, resting on much-disturbed
Coal Measure shales. The boulders in this gravel consisted mainly of
Carboniferous sandstones and grits, but there were also brown and black
flints, fossiliferous Magnesian Limestone, red quartzite (probably derived from the Bunter), Shap granite and decomposed basalt.

This deposit is believed to have been formed in a lake, retained at its
east end by a glacier in the Vale of York.

At Pledwick, 3 miles south-east of Horbury, Green and Russell found
" pebbles of Carboniferous Sandstone, Carboniferous Limestone, Trap,

[6]Proc. Yorks. Geol. Soc., vol. vi, 1879, p. 95.
[7]The Naturalist, 1902, p. 214.
[8]The Naturalist, 1915, p. 125.

Fig. 17.

SECTION NEAR STAINCROSS (after A. H. Green).

a. Upper Boulder Clay. *b.* Warp, with Sand and Gravel at the north end. *c.* Lower Boulder Clay. *d.* Carboniferous Rocks.

and Syenite, and a large boulder of highly altered Breccia, at a height
of 150 feet above the sea." They found " syenite " also at Notton
Green, and Shap granite at Royston.

We come, finally, to the glacial drift, 300 feet above sea-level, at
Staincross station, 6 miles south-south-east of Horbury, and 2 miles
north of Barnsley.

The section here was described by A. H. Green in 1876.[9]

The section (fig. 17), is that of a valley carved out of Coal Measure
sandstone, and filled in with boulder clay. As measured on Green and
Russell's drawing, the valley is 480 yards across and 100 feet deep. The
lateral junction of the sandstone with the clay is very much shattered,
and large blocks of the rock are embedded in the clay. The section at
a point half-way across the valley showed : —

	Ft.	Ins.
Upper boulder clay, ...	13	0
Seam of warp, ...	0	2
Upper boulder clay, ...	9	0
Warp, ...	9	0
Fine gravel and sand, not bottomed, ...	5	0

On the south side of the section, a lower boulder clay directly underlies the upper boulder clay. This lower boulder clay " is blue, very stiff,
somewhat gritty, and without the least trace of bedding. The stones
are mostly small, but a large block occurs every here and there; the
majority have their angles and edges blunted; some are quite angular;
a few are well-rounded pebbles. By far the larger quantity, probably
99 per cent., are Coal-measure rocks, chiefly sandstone, after which the
most numerous are flat, blunted slabs of well-scratched black shale; bits
of coal were not uncommon. Foreign stones, though not plentiful, were
easy to find. Carboniferous Limestone (ice-scratched), chert, and black
earthy limestone were the most conspicuous, and a specimen was found
of blue, close-grained trap, with crystals of iron pyrites."

The upper boulder clay " is by no means so stiff a clay as the lower
bed. It is more sandy and there are fewer stones in it. It contains
irregular, interbedded masses of Warp (laminated clay), and nests and
lenticular sheets of sand and gravel. The whole is rudely bedded, and
the beds are in places very sharply contorted. The clay is traversed by
curved joints or cracks, with polished faces, filled in with sand, along
which great masses break off."

The warp in the measured section " is a bluish-brown, very finely
laminated, tough clay, with small well-rounded pebbles of carboniferous
sandstone and coal; the bedding was unmistakable, but wavy and
irregular.

" The gravel at the bottom of the cutting was mostly small, but it
contained a few large angular boulders of sandstone."

At the north end, the lower boulder clay reappears in the bottom of
the section, and here the warp " seems to be replaced by some fine sand

⁹*Proc. Yorks. Geol. Soc.*, vol. vi, 1879, p. 122. This account is reprinted in Green
and Russell's *Geology of the Yorkshire Coalfield*, 1878, p. 776, and Pl. 26.
The above particulars are taken from these sources.

and sandstone gravel, in lenticular beds, with nests and layers of broken coal; embedded in this gravel were some very large angular blocks of sandstone, and at its base was a layer of angular bits of black shale, some of which was ice-scratched.

"The patch of Boulder Clay exposed in the section just described seems to extend nearly as far as Carlton on the east and beyond Royston on the north-east. No other sections of importance were obtained, but the ground is everywhere stiff and clayey, and thickly sprinkled with erratics. A large number of the blocks are hard calliardy sandstone and ganister, but foreigners were plentiful enough. They included sundry kinds of Trap, highly metamorphosed breccias, quartzite, and white vein-quartz; encrinital chert also was not rare."

Important additions to the list of erratics in these boulder clays were later recorded by W. Hemingway;[10] they include grey granite, andesitic ash, vesicular lava, rhyolite, grey encrinital limestone, Liassic limestone with *Gryphaea incurva*, fine gneissose granite, Magnesian Limestone, and white quartz from the Millstone Grit.

CHAPTER XXII.

BALBY.

Speaking some months ago with Mr Furnival, of Doncaster, our conversation turned upon glacial deposits, and Mr Furnival stated that the clay in a clay-pit two miles south-west of Doncaster, and known as Balby Brick Works, appeared to be of the nature of a " boulder clay."

T. H. EASTERFIELD, 1883.

Easterfield appears to have been the first to describe the clay with boulders, at Balby. This he did, with much attention to details, in a paper of less than a page in length, communicated to the Yorkshire Geological Society in 1883.[1]

Of this deposit, he says: "It consists of a tough dark-blue clay, packed with boulders up to half-a-ton in weight. The boulders are mainly of local origin, magnesian-limestone, clay-ironstone, and coal-measure shales and sandstones being most abundant; though not unfrequently carboniferous limestone and upper permian marl with gypsum are found, as are also a few small boulders of haematite. One very small block appears to be of the nature of a quartz-felsite. Very many of the boulders are beautifully scratched and polished by the action of the ice.

"From a boring made some years ago it appears that this clay is sixty feet in thickness."

"The clay consists of two parts, an upper and a lower, and the surface of the lower appears to have been smoothed by the ice before

---

[10]*The Naturalist*, 1894, p. 299.
[1]*Proc. Yorks. Geol. Soc.*, vol. viii, 1882-1884, p. 212.

the upper was deposited. This division in the clay seems to indicate a cessation in the glacial action, but there is no distinctive difference between the boulders of the upper and those of the lower clay, though there is rather more magnesian limestone in the lower than in the upper."

A similar dual division has been noticed in another pit at Balby; where a bed, about a foot thick, of coarse sand of Millstone Grit type, and containing numerous fragments of coal, with a few rounded carboniferous boulders, was seen about 12 feet below the surface. The clay above and below it was of the usual character.[2]

In the pit first mentioned, H. H. Corbett and P. F. Kendall[3] found 30 or 40 igneous rocks, all andesites and andesitic breccias of Lake District types, except one which was the quartz-porphyry of St. John's, and another a red granite of unknown derivation. Corbett[4] later reported a specimen of basalt.

Corbett and Kendall describe the clay as " wholly unstratified." It was regarded by the Rev. W. L. Carter[5] as having been formed by a glacier moving down the Vale of York.

" The clay rests upon a planed-off surface of very red Triassic sandstone, or rather soft incoherent sand. How did the ice-sheet pass over such a material without disturbing it by shearing stresses? "[6]

In a specimen of this deposit, examined by myself, the clay was distinctly foliated, and had the same colour as the York brick-clay. After washing the sample, and drying the residual sand, a considerable amount of wood or coal was got from it by flotation in carbon tetrachloride; affording additional evidence that the deposit was formed under still-water conditions.

Of the transparent minerals in the sand, having a specific gravity greater than 2.72, the most abundant were muscovite and barytes; and, in a lesser degree, chlorite. Other minerals were in altogether subordinate amount, namely: zircon (some rounded and dusky grains may have been xenotime), brown tourmaline, colourless garnet, apatite and staurolite, in roughly that order of frequency. Garnet was rare, or very rare; apatite and staurolite extremely rare. One grain of actinolite was noted, and another was probably of andalusite.

Thus it will be seen that the minerals common in the Trias are an insignificant part of the whole; while those of the Permian predominate.[7]

The petrographical evidence, therefore, shows that this deposit (or a part of it) was laid down in still water, and that the material came from the west, rather than the north.

[2]H. H. Corbett. *The Naturalist*, 1898, p. 355.

[3]*The Naturalist*, 1897, pp. 68, 69.

[4]*The Naturalist*, 1898, p. 355.

[5]*Proc. Yorks. Geol. Soc.*, vol. xv, 1905, p. 417.

[6]Kendall, P. F., and H. E. Wroot, *Geology of Yorkshire*, 1924, p. 922.

[7]On the minerals of the Trias, see F. Smithson, *Proc. Geol. Assoc.*, vol. xlii, 1931, p. 125; and on those of the Permian, H. P. Lewis, *Geol. Mag.*, 1923, p. 307; and H. C. Versey, *Proc. Yorks. Geol. Soc.*, vol. xx, 1925, p. 200.

Fig. 18.
MAP SHOWING THE POSITION OF KENDALL AND WROOT'S ICE-FRONTS.
(Scale : ¼-inch to 1 mile).

CHAPTER XXIII.

THE LEEDS HIPPOPOTAMUS.

The discovery of Hippopotamus in such a nearly perfect and unrolled condition in the superficial deposits of the river Aire, at Leeds, was a most fortunate thing for geologists who discuss the later Quaternary deposits. . . .
A. TYLOR, 1868.

In 1852, the remains of not less than three individuals of Hippopotamus were discovered at Leeds, close to Holbeck station, at the angle formed between Wortley Beck and the River Aire, 115 feet above sea-level. In one case the skeleton was nearly complete and the cranium, vertebrae, ribs and bones of the extremities were all found lying in their proper relative position.

The first account of this discovery appears to be that by H. Denny, published in 1854.[1] As it is of the greatest importance to ascertain the nature of the deposit in which these bones were found, and to determine, as nearly as may be, its relation to other beds, the following passages are taken from it.

" These remains were found at a depth of 9 feet in a bed of clay, and 20 feet above the present bed of the river. This bed of clay, along with sand and gravel, which at distances of even a few yards pass and repass into each other, constitute an extensive flat deposit in the lower valley of the Aire, commencing a little above Leeds, and extending along the valley of the Aire, varying in breadth from one to three miles, until it becomes continuous with a similar deposit in the valley of the Calder.

" At Leeds this flat valley formation rests upon the outbreak of the coal measures. It consists of clay, sand, and gravel, irregularly deposited under the varied influences of currents and eddies, and forming in the neighbourhood of Leeds a deposit averaging from 10 to 20 feet in thickness. The gravel is chiefly formed of millstone-grit and other sandstones, with occasional portions of mountain limestone, from the strata traversed by the river in the upper part of its course.

" Along with the remains of Hippopotamus have been found in this valley deposit the bones of the Elephant, of two bovine animals, apparently the *Bos latifrons* and *Bos primigenius*, of the *Cervus elaphus*, *Equus caballus*, *Capra hircus* (?), and *Sus scrofa*. Associated with them are laid horizontally the trunks of trees, as the oak, fir, and others, and hazel-nuts."

In another paper,[2] Denny gives a complete list of the bones, and states that they were found in their natural position; otherwise this account contains much less information than the earlier one.

[1]*Rept. Brit. Assoc. for* 1853 (1854), p. 51.
[2]*Proc. Yorks. Geol. Soc.*, vol. iii, 1859, p. 321.

A paper by T. P. Teale, published in 1859,[3] adds little to our knowledge of the mammalia, but is of interest for the description of the superficial deposits of the district with which he concludes.   After describing blue and yellow boulder clays, he takes up the subject of the warp clay in which the vertebrate remains were found, and which overlies the boulder clays.   " The warp," he says, " is spread over the valley of the Aire, producing a flat-looking surface, gently sloping upwards at the sides of the valley, and downwards towards the estuary. At the sides of the Vale of Leeds, the warp shelves off a little below the sea-level of 150 feet, and is not found higher than this level in the immediate neighbourhood of Leeds. Prolongation of the warp may be traced up all the little tributaries of the Aire in this district as high as to the level of 150 feet, or thereabouts.

" The characters of the warp deposit are very variable. It sometimes approaches to a tolerably pure blue or yellow clay, but generally it is much more earthy and dirty-looking than the clays before described. In many localities it is very sandy, and indeed passes into sand and gravel, more especially in the central parts of the valley. It contains stones of very variable character, some angular and subangular, derived from no great distance; others rounded, polished, and far-travelled. It contains much vegetable matter, as roots and fibres. Drifted wood, chiefly oak, is found in great abundance in it; also the fir, the hazel, and abundance of leaves and nuts."[4]

Leaving Holbeck, and going 5 miles down the river, we reach Woodlesford, situated on the right bank, at the foot of rising ground at the top of which stands Rothwell Haigh with the gravels described in an earlier chapter.

Deposits occur here which, in constitution and height above the river, agree with those at Holbeck; though no fossils have been found in them.

A series of excavations at Woodlesford have been described by A. Gilligan,[5] of which the following is typical : —

	Ft.	Ins.
Surface soil, ...	1	2
Brown laminated clay, ...	5	0
Sand and loam, ...	3	2
Strong slaty brown laminated clay, ...	5	10
Gravel, ...	1	8
Sand, ..., ...	3	8
Black sand with manganese dioxide, ...	2	8
Total depth of foundations, ...	23	2

The height of the solid rock is 44 feet O.D.

The sands here are like those at Rothwell Haigh, though manganese dioxide has not been seen there. The gravel also is similar, consisting

[3] Rept. Brit. Assoc. for 1858 (1859), p. 111.
[4] A few further details regarding the Holbeck deposit will be found in a paper by A. Tylor in Q.J.G.S., vol. xxv, 1869, pp. 64-65.
[5] Proc. Yorks. Geol. Soc., vol. xix, 1918, p. 255.

of Coal Measure sandstone and grit, large numbers of ironstone nodules, and a little chert.   The largest stone measured about 6 x 3 x 2 inches.

The laminated clays, especially the top bed, contain " race."

The Rothwell gravels are at a height of 200 feet above the sea, and the Woodlesford deposit is at between 60 and 70 feet; thus it is clear, as pointed out by Gilligan, " that a great interval of time must be represented between the period when the Rothwell gravels and clays were formed and that at which those at Woodlesford were deposited." And of the latter he says: " The deposits are undoubtedly of deltaic origin, laid down in a lake or pool, and are not such as are ordinarily formed by rivers in such a part of their course.   The lacustrine conditions may have been due to the blocking of the mouth of the Humber by the North Sea ice at one stage of the last Glacial period."

CHAPTER XXIV.

THE DISTRICT BETWEEN MASHAM AND KNARESBOROUGH.

No one accustomed to reason on the waste of the surface evidenced by the excavations of valleys, and to consider the present detached masses of strata as the remains of continuous deposits, the present hills and ridges as parts of a once unbroken surface, can be surprised at the notion that waters have formerly run and channels been scooped out in directions quite different from those taken by existing streams; but it must always appear strange that waters should have flowed across what now are and must always have been natural valleys and ridges. . . .

JOHN PHILLIPS, 1836.

We now enter a district of great interest, and one to which several investigators have devoted much attention.

In 1873, Fox-Strangways[1] observed that the drift here is divisible into two kinds; a local drift, containing stones from rocks which occur in the immediate neighbourhood *in situ*, and in which pebbles of Carboniferous Limestone are almost if not entirely absent; and an erratic drift in which such pebbles are abundant.   The line dividing these two sorts of drift follows the valleys of the Crimple and the Nidd as far as Ripley, and then turns northward, along the narrow gorge in which Cayton Gill flows.

The erratic drift is clearly the product of a glacier which moved down the Vale of York from the north.   We have already seen it was such a glacier which deposited the terminal moraines at Escrick and York.

By plotting on a map the position of certain moraines and deserted valleys, Kendall and Wroot[2] have recognised two stages in the retreat of the western edge of this glacier, which they consider may no doubt be associated with the terminal moraines already mentioned.

[1]*Geology of Country N. and E. of Harrogate*, 1st ed., 1873, p. 13.
[2]Kendall, P. F., and H. E. Wroot, *Geology of Yorkshire*, 1924, pp. 539-555.

First: let us follow the course of the ice-edge which they believe is connected with the Escrick moraine. The ice at this stage blocked the east end of Coverdale, forming a lake which overflowed through a nick in the hills half a mile due west of Witton Fell Plantation (7 miles W.N.W. of Masham). By the same agency, lakes were formed in Colsterdale and the valley of Pott Beck (4 miles W. of Masham). The water from these ran through channels in the Druid's Temple Plantation into small lakes at the head of Cat Gill and Wreakes Beck. The head of Dallow Gill was in the same condition, but it is uncertain through which channel this lake overflowed. The waters in the upper reaches of Skell Gill were similarly ponded back, and overflowed through a channel near Eavestone, and thence along Picking Gill. Kendall and Wroot are uncertain whether, at this stage of the glaciation, the drainage-water escaped by way of Haddockstones Grange and Dole Bank into Cayton Gill, and so into the Nidd at Ripley; or along a line further west of Cayton Gill. Having traced the line of drainage thus far, they remark, "the channels become successively larger and larger as the series is traced southward. This might be expected, since at each stage the total drainage area—both of hill-tops and of the ice—would be considerably increased and consequently the water passing through the channels must have been more and more copious. But Cayton Gill, impressive though it is, lacks something of the proportions which might have been expected if it operated as the main channel of the whole of the Ure waters throughout the earlier period as well as during a great part of the later stage when the ice was in retreat. Some alternative route for the waters which came by way of Eavestone may, therefore, have existed, though none has yet been discovered."

From Ripley, or thereabouts, Kendall and Wroot trace the ice-edge to Knaresborough. The ice, lying across the valley of the Nidd, formed a moraine at Nidd Hall and impounded the upper waters, which " sought a new outlet and cut a notch so deep that even when the ice was removed the river kept to this course rather than return to its old bed." The notch is the gorge at Knaresborough; the old bed of the Nidd is traceable through Brearton, Farnham and Tewit Mires.

Below Knaresborough, these authors consider that the position of the ice-edge of this period is marked by the dry valley running from North Deighton to Kirk Deighton; and at Wetherby it is indicated by the phenomenon of the Wharfe diversion. The River Wharfe approaches the town of Wetherby from the south; and then, turning south-eastward, flows through a gorge to Thorp Arch. Thence it runs to Tadcaster, along the south side of the Escrick moraine, and joins the River Ouse above Cawood. That the " gorge at Wetherby is a diversion due to the Vale of York glacier is evident from the fact, revealed in boreholes, that the ground upon which the town of Wetherby stands, obstructing the natural line of the river, is wholly of boulder-clay to a depth of over 50 feet."[3]

[3]Kendall and Wroot, op. cit., p. 545.

So much, then, for the ice-edge which Kendall and Wroot associate with the Escrick moraine.

Second: let us go northward once more and trace that which they connect with the moraine at York.

At High Sutton, 2 miles north-west of Masham, there are dry channels; and others corresponding with them are to be found in Swinton Park, on the south side of the River Burn. Just south of Swinton, the ice-edge is marked by a moraine across Roomer Common. The sharp deflection of the River Laver, at Winksley, is regarded as a glacial diversion; and south of this place the channels through Sun Wood and Spa Gill Wood define the ice-edge. The line of drainage continued through the Dene, near Sawley Hall, to Cayton Gill, which, " whether it existed or not at the earlier period, was the natural and only overflow southward of the waters of this edge of the Vale of York glacier." Here Kendall and Wroot bring to an end their description of the second ice-front, and take up the consideration of certain indications of a third.

They believe the River Ure formerly ran eastward from Low Rookwith, and that the present course of the river below that village is " due to the shouldering up of the Ure into the foot of the Pennines as a consequence of the presence of a great thickness of ice in the plain."

" The anomalous position of the modern river Ure becomes marked south of Masham, where the river enters and runs for two miles through a gorge famous as Hackfall."[4]

A little east of Mickley, a dry valley between Carr House and Spring Wood marks the ice-edge. The southward continuation of this valley is known as Thieves Gill, which runs down to the River Laver. South of the river, this line of drainage is continued by a dry valley bounded on its east side by a moraine. This valley runs past Low Lindrick to Studley Royal; and here Kendall and Wroot conclude their description of the third ice-front.

CHAPTER XXV.

JOINTS.

The jointed structure . . . is an essential and necessary part of the structure of rocks, not to be viewed in the light of geological accidents, depending on subterranean movements, but affording evidence by the constancy of its direction in large districts, of the action of some very general cause, capable of controlling the consolidation of the rocks so as to cause the separation of the condensed masses along certain parallels.

JOHN PHILLIPS, 1836.

L'influence topographique des diaclases se manifeste très-souvent sur un échelle beaucoup plus grande. Plus on étudie, sur des cartes exactes, le dessin

4op. cit., p. 554.

général des vallées et le relief du sol, plus on y reconnaît, de toutes parts, même dans les pays dont les couches sont restées à peu près horizontales, de nombreux traits rectilignes, parallèles et souvent coudés. Or, ce caractère, sur lequel l'un de nos plus savant topographes, M. le colonel du génie Goulier, a appelé l'attention, se montre très-fréquemment en rapport avec les diaclases.

A. DAUBREE, 1879.

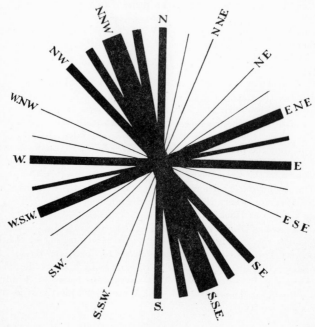

Fig. 19.

PHILLIPS' JOINT-PLANE DIAGRAM.

In 1823, and again in 1828, John Phillips turned his attention to a consideration of the joint-planes in rocks, and the direction which they maintain across country. But his main exposition on the subject is to be found in Part II of his Illustrations of the Geology of Yorkshire, published in 1836. He expressed his results by means of the diagram reproduced in fig. 19, in which the thickness of the lines is proportional to the frequency of occurrence. It will be seen at once that most frequently the joint-planes run in a N.N.W.-S.S.E. direction. The axis of the Vale of York follows this direction, and so does the course of the River Ure from Rookwith to Hackfall. The same is true of the channel running past Low Lindrick to Studley Royal.

Picking Gill, Spa Gill, and the channel from Mickley to Spring Wood are parallel to another joint-plane direction.

The course of many streams and rivers is governed by the direction of joint-planes, even to the smallest detail. Take Cayton Gill as an

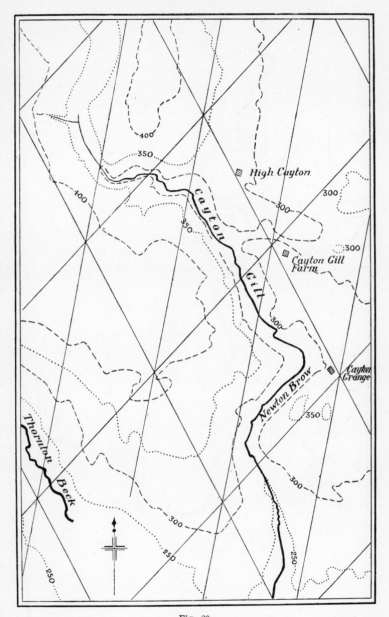

Fig. 20.

MAP OF CAYTON GILL.

Showing the Relation between the Course of the Valley and the Joint-planes.
(Scale : 3 inches to 1 mile).

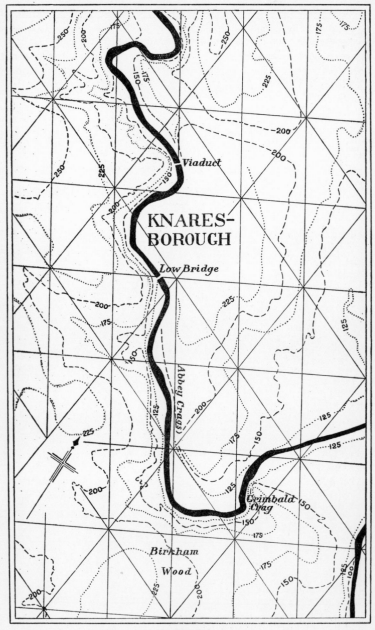

Fig. 21.
MAP OF THE KNARESBOROUGH GEORGE.
Showing the Relation between the Course of the River and the Joint-planes.
(Scale : 3 inches to 1 mile).

example. On inspection of fig. 20 it will be seen that the stream runs S.S.E. from High Cayton to Cayton Grange; here it turns suddenly to the south-west, and after running past Newton Brow, reverts to its south-south-easterly direction. The network of lines represents the direction of the joint-planes in this district, and it will be seen that each reach of the stream is parallel to a joint.

The course of the River Nidd at Knaresborough affords another instance of the same kind. In fig. 21 the thick sinuous line represents the river and the network of fine lines indicates the traces of the joint-planes. It is at once evident that every part of the river's course is determined by the joint-planes. And this must have been the case for a considerable time past, for even the 200-ft. contour-line follows these directions very closely.

Fig. 22.

MAP OF THE DISTRICT AROUND MASHAM.

The thick interrupted lines indicate part of Kendall and Wroot's Ice-fronts.

(Scale : ½-inch to 1 mile).

CHAPTER XXVI.

THE DISTRICT BETWEEN MASHAM AND KNARESBOROUGH RECONSIDERED.

The Drifts themselves play a comparatively insignificant part in the formation of our scenery, for the great features that our country now possesses were nearly all marked out before the Drifts were deposited.

H. B. WOODWARD, 1876.

At the period when this Till was formed the general contour of the ground must have been pretty much as it is now, although a large amount of denudation has taken place since the Glacial epoch; by this we mean that all the present valleys and streams are preglacial although they may have been filled up and cut afresh in later times.

A. H. GREEN AND R. RUSSELL, 1878.

In the last chapter we saw that certain valleys and dry channels may have a more fundamental origin than that suggested by the glacial theory.   It was pointed out that the axis of the Vale of York runs roughly in a N.N.W.-S.S.E. direction; any glacier moving down it would often have its lateral margins similarly aligned.   A joint-plane also follows this direction.   Channels thus orientated require close scrutiny before they can be recognised as of truly glacial origin.

According to Kendall and Wroot's interpretation, the course of the River Ure below Rookwith is due to glacial diversion.   The same matter has been expounded by Raistrick,[1] as follows: " The valley around Masham, its tributary Colsterdale, the valley of the River Burn, and the cut through the scarp at Tanfield are, however, plainly Pre-Glacial by their relation to the drift deposits.   The Pre-Glacial Ure, however, flowed due east from Leyburn by the wide and mature valley which continues the line of Upper Wensleydale to the Vale of York, by Snape.   In Pre-Glacial times, the Burn was flowing through the Tanfield gap in the Magnesian Limestone with its northern tributary joining it at Masham, flowing on what is now the line of the Ure from about Clifton.   The rock bar across the valley at Hackfall is at 300 ft. O.D. and it is probable that the lowering of this and the steep gradient of the River Burn would together have caused the northern tributary from Masham to cut back north of Clifton, and so capture the Ure in the normal way of river capture.   The Ice Age came, however, before this was accomplished.   When the easterly course of the Ure was blocked by the Vale of York ice a very slight ponding of the water caused an overflow by this valley, and the lowering of the already slight water-shed by the passage of the Wensleydale glacier over it, followed by the dumping of

[1]*Proc. Yorks. Geol. Soc.,* vol. xx, 1926, pp. 405-406.

thick boulder clay and moraine across the mouth of Wensleydale made
the diversion permanent."

In Raistrick's view, then, the valley below Clifton is due to normal
fluviatile erosion; a conclusion in consonance with the fact that it follows
a joint-direction. It may be pointed out, incidentally, that there is no
evidence to prove that the northern tributary of the River Burn did not
capture the Ure, in the normal way of river capture, before the glaciation.

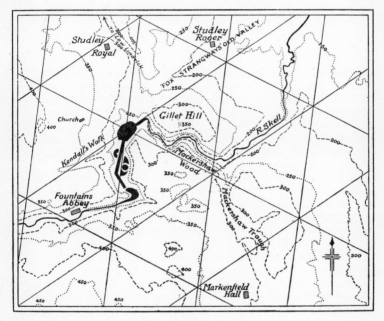

Fig. 23.

MAP OF STUDLEY PARK.

Showing the Relation between the Course of the River and the Joint-planes.
(Scale : 1½ inches to 1 mile).

The channel at Low Lindrick is undoubtedly due to lateral drainage
along an ice-edge; for although it runs parallel to a joint-direction, it
is bounded on the east by a moraine. But even in this case, it is difficult
to determine the lie of the ice-edge to the south. The nature of the
problem will be rendered clearer on referring to fig. 23.

Fox-Strangways,[2] describing the old course of the River Skell,
remarks: " after traversing the grounds of Fountains Abbey, it flowed
north and east across Studley Park; this valley becoming blocked by
Glacial beds, it cut the present picturesque channel through the

2Geology of Country N. and E. of Harrogate, 2nd ed., 1908, p. 31.

Magnesian Limestone in Mackershaw Woods to the east of the great lake."

The topography of Studley Park is, then, precisely the same as that of Knaresborough. In the first case, we have the old course of the Skell running, from the lake, round the north side of Gillet Hill. In the second case, as a corresponding feature, there is the old valley of the Nidd running from Nidd Hall through Brearton, Farnham and Tewit Mires. And at Studley Park there is the ravine in Mackershaw Woods corresponding to the gorge at Knaresborough. It is therefore not surprising that Fox-Strangways should explain the origin of the Mackershaw Wood channel in the same way as Kendall had that at Knaresborough.

In dealing with the phenomena at Studley, however, Kendall and Wroot view the matter differently. They consider that at one time the drainage from the west was along a channel known as Kendall's Walk, though "the occupation of this channel was but a brief episode; the Skell soon became open, and the glacial waters of the whole Ure system then coursed through the gorge of Fountains Abbey. Apparently the course now followed by the Skell through Studley Park did not become available immediately. The waters ponded back over the site of the ornamental lakes, and overflowed south-eastward along the ice-edge by an ill-defined channel running down to Markenfield Hall.

"At some stage not clearly ascertained there was hollowed out the singularly straight channel followed by the main drive in Studley Park from the neighbourhood of the church to Studley Roger."[3]

The valley of the Skell was, then, in existence before the glaciation, and needed only to be unstopped for the whole drainage from the north to escape thereby.

There can be little doubt the history of the valleys in Studley Park is the same as of those between Ripley and Knaresborough. The only point to be settled is whether Kendall and Wroot's treatment of the case at Studley Park applies to both; or whether each is to be interpreted along the lines they have indicated in the case at Knaresborough.

Their explanation of the origin of the Knaresborough gorge is that it was excavated by the waters flowing along the foot of the ice-sheet as it lay at Knaresborough. If it were true, we should expect to find a notch in the cliff between Birkham Wood and Grimbald Crag. There is none; but, instead, the valley turns abruptly to the north-east; a fact not readily explained by the glacial theory, but one which literally "falls into line" when joint-planes are taken into consideration.

Again; the formation of the Knaresborough gorge involved the cutting away of a thickness of 100 feet of rock. Could this amount of erosion have been effected during the time the ice-sheet lay stationary at Knaresborough? For an answer to this question we may turn back to the channel at Low Lindrick; for it is undoubtedly of glacial origin; the lateral moraine is there to attest the fact. The bottom of the Low

[3]Kendall and Wroot, *op. cit.*, p. 553. The channel mentioned in the last paragraph is Fox-Strangways' old channel of the Skell.

Lindrick channel is not more than 50 feet below the high ground to the west of it.

The Knaresborough gorge is not, then, of glacial origin. Both it and the valley of the River Skell in Mackershaw Wood were already in existence before the glaciation. This is true also of the Cayton Gill valley.

Since all these three channels follow the direction of joint-planes, it may safely be concluded they are the products of normal fluviatile erosion.

CHAPTER XXVII.

THE WHARFE DIVERSION.

The irregular accumulation of the glacial deposits produced many changes in the courses of the rivers. . . .

P. F. KENDALL, 1896.

As Kendall and Wroot have observed, the impounded waters at Studley Park " overflowed south-eastward along the ice-edge by an ill-defined channel running down to Markenfield Hall." This channel, the bottom of which is just below 300 feet O.D., is the last piece of indubitable evidence we now have of erosion contemporaneous with the high-level glaciation of the district north of Knaresborough.

The overflow of waters which approached Knaresborough from the south-west has been traced by Raistrick,[1] who concludes that " at this stage these channels debouched into a lake held up by the Vale of York Ice draining south at probably just over 200 ft. O.D. on the line now taken by the Crimple." Though this statement is unsupported by any evidence of lake-deposits, there are channels which seem to have approached a local base-level at between 300 and 200 feet O.D. Whether this 200 ft. stage is connected either directly or indirectly with that at Wingate Hill is a matter which cannot be settled till more work has been done. But it is obvious that there is no relation between it and the York and Escrick moraines. For if, as Kendall and Wroot assert, the line of the Escrick moraine is continued through Kirk Deighton to Knaresborough, it is clear that, on the melting of the ice, brick-clay could not have been deposited between Goldsborough and Ribston. The Goldsborough brick-clay, as we saw in Chapter XVI, belongs to the period of the York and Escrick moraines; the Knaresborough gorge does not.

On the retreat of the ice from the Escrick-Kirk Deighton position, to that represented by the moraine at Cowthorpe, the intervening

[1] *Proc. Yorks. Geol. Soc.*, vol. xxii, 1931, p. 27.

district was left awash.   This includes Ingmanthorpe Park and the
ground on which Wetherby stands; nearly all of which is just below 100
feet O.D.   The Nidd and the Wharfe were then confluent; the ultimate
course of the latter river was not determined till the withdrawal of the
ice from Cowthorpe.   During the period of confluence, the fate of the
River Wharfe was in a very delicate balance.   Having still to negotiate
a sharp bend at Collingham, its velocity would be checked, and this would
tend to set up aggradation.   On the other hand, in the case of the
Nidd, the conditions would be slightly in favour of erosion; the course
of that river being comparatively straight.   On the retreat of the ice
from Cowthorpe, some such slight advantage turned the balance in
favour of the River Nidd; leaving the Wharfe cut off at Wetherby by a
bar only a few feet in height.

CHAPTER XXVIII.

KIRKDALE, OVERTON AND BIELSBECK.

. . . our Yorkshire Hyaenopolis. . . .

W. BUCKLAND, 1841.

Three mammalian deposits remain to be described; and since the age
of none of them can, at present, be determined with certainty, they may
as well be considered together.

The cave at Kirkdale is situated 1½ miles west-south-west of Kirby
Moorside, on the north side of the Vale of Pickering.   The most complete account of this cavern and its contents is that by William Buckland;[1] and the following quotations are taken from it.

"It was not till the summer of 1821 that the existence of any animal
remains, or of the cavern containing them, was suspected.   At this
time, in continuing the operations of a large quarry along the slope just
mentioned, the workmen accidentally intersected the mouth of a long
hole or cavern, closed externally with rubbish, and overgrown with grass
and bushes.   As this rubbish was removed before any competent person
had examined it, it is not certain whether it was composed of diluvial
gravel and rolled pebbles, or was simply the debris that had fallen from
the softer portions of the strata that lay above it; the workmen, however, who removed it, and some gentlemen who saw it, assure me that
it was composed of gravel and sand.   In the interior of the cave I

---

[1]*Reliquiae Diluvianae,* 1823, pp. 1-51.   It would seem that " Mr Harrison, a
   medical gentleman of Kirby Moorside," was the first to appreciate the importance of this discovery.   Among others who were early at work was
   William Salmond, a surgeon, of York.   He appears again in connection
   with the deposit at Bielsbeck.

could not find a single rolled pebble, nor have I seen in all the collections that have been taken from it one bone, or fragment of bone, that bears the slightest mark of having been rolled by the action of water."

" On entering the cave at Kirkdale, the first thing observed was a sediment of soft mud or loam, covering entirely its whole bottom to the average depth of about a foot, and concealing the subjacent rock, or actual floor of the cavern. Not a particle of mud was found attached either to the sides or roof; nor was there a trace of it adhering to the sides or upper portions of the transverse fissures, or anything to suggest the idea that it had entered through them. The surface of this sediment when the cave was first opened was nearly smooth and level, except in those parts where its regularity had been broken by the accumulation of stalagmite above it, or ruffled by the dripping of water: its substance is an argillaceous and slightly micaceous loam, composed of such minute particles as would easily be suspended in muddy water, and mixed with much calcareous matter, that seems to have been derived in part from the dripping of the roof, and in part from comminuted bones. At about 100 feet within the cave's mouth the sediment became more coarse and sandy, and partially covered with an incrustation of black manganese ore."

" There is no alternation of mud with any repeated beds of stalactite, but simply a partial deposit of the latter on the floor beneath it; and it was chiefly in the lower part of the earthy sediment, and in the stalagmitic matter beneath it, that the animal remains were found: there was nowhere any black earth or admixture of animal matter, except an infinity of extremely minute particles of undecomposed bone. In the whole extent of the cave, only a very few large bones have been discovered that are tolerably perfect; most of them are broken into small angular fragments and chips, the greater part of which lay separately in the mud, whilst others were wholly or partially invested with stalagmite; and others again mixed with masses of still smaller fragments and cemented by stalagmite, so as to form an osseous breccia. In some few places where the mud was shallow, and the heaps of teeth and bones considerable, parts of the latter were elevated some inches above the surface of the mud and its stalagmitic crust, and the upper ends of the bones thus projecting like the legs of pigeons through a pie-crust into the void space above, have become thinly covered with stalagmitic drippings. . . ."

The bones, as since determined by Lydekker,[2] were those of: *Felis leo, Hyaena crocuta, Canis lupus, Vulpes vulpes, Ursus spelaeus, U. arctus, U. arctos horribilis, Mustela erminea, M. nivalis, Lepus europaeus, L. cuniculus, Microtus amphibius, M. agrestis, Mus musculus, Cervus giganteus, C. elaphus, Rangifer tarandus, Bos taurus, Bos (Bison) priscus, Hippopotamus amphibius, Sus scrofa* (?), *Rhinoceros antiquitatis, R. leptorhinus, Equus caballus, Elephas primigenius, E. antiquus.*

[2] R. Lydekker, in *Victoria County History of York,* vol. i, 1907, pp. 100-101.

While of birds, the following were found: *Corvus corax, Alauda arvensis, Columba* sp., *Bernicla brenta, Perdix perdix, Scolopax gallinago.*

" The greatest number of teeth," wrote Buckland, " are those of hyænas, and the ruminantia. Mr Gibson alone collected more than 300 canine teeth of the hyæna, which at the least must have belonged to 75 individuals, and adding to these the canine teeth I have seen in other collections, I cannot calculate the total number of hyænas of which there is evidence, at less than 200 or 300."

" It must already appear probable, from the facts above described, particularly from the comminuted state and apparently gnawed condition of the bones, that the cave at Kirkdale was, during a long succession of years, inhabited as a den by hyænas, and that they dragged into its recesses the other animal bodies whose remains are found mixed indiscriminately with their own."

The only clues to the age of this cave deposit, which Buckland's account affords, are in the statement that the materials which hid the mouth of the cave were probably gravel and sand; and " a further argument may be drawn from the limited quantity of postdiluvian stalactite, as well as from the undecayed condition of the bones, to show that the time elapsed since the introduction of the diluvial mud has not been one of excessive length. . . ."

About 1818, James Cook, of York, discovered mammalian remains at Overton, on the left bank of the River Ouse, 4 miles above that city. The bones were found 30 feet beneath the surface, in dark red clay below 4 feet of rolled gravel, the upper part of the section being chiefly pale red sand. This red sand at the top was doubtless left behind by the ice on its retreat from York at the end of the last glaciation.

The ground at Overton is part of a dissected peneplain standing about 50 to 60 feet above sea-level, and 30 feet above the alluvial flat of the river.

The list of bones given by Fox-Strangways[3] is: *Elephas primigenius, Rhinoceros tichorhinus,* Stag, Reindeer, Horse; also bones of tiger, elk, and bird.

Phillips and some others record Hippopotamus from this place; there are, however, no remains of this animal in the Cook Collection.[4]

The above assemblage of animals is similar to that found in the Second River Terrace of the Warwickshire Avon, which stands 30 to 40 feet above the river.[5]

A farm known as Bielsbeck lies 3 miles east of Holme upon Spalding Moor and 2½ miles south-south-west of Market Weighton. A mammaliferous marl was discovered here by a farmer named Foster; though " the merit of first calling attention to it belongs in a great degree to Mr William Hey Dikes of Hull."[6]

[3] *Geology of Country N. and E. of Harrogate*, 2nd ed., 1908, p. 24.
[4] In the Museum of the Yorkshire Philosophical Society, together with the MS. Catalogue. The few remaining specimens are fragmentary and water-worn.
[5] M. E. Tomlinson, *Q.J.G.S.*, vol. lxxxi, 1925, p. 137.
[6] J. Phillips, *Geology of Yorks.*, Part 1, 2nd ed., 1835, p. 143.

It was first described by Vernon Harcourt in 1829; the bones being identified by William Salmond.[7] Many years later, a committee of the British Association reported on the subject.[8]

The succession of beds exposed in excavations at this place is clearly presented in the section given by Vernon Harcourt:

MINERAL CONTENTS.	Depth in Ft.	ORGANIC CONTENTS.
Yellow sand. In this and the gravel below it a few pebbles of quartz and sandstone.	3	No bones, shells, or vegetable remains in the sand or gravel.
Gravel composed of chalk pebbles and sharp flints.	4½	
Grey marl indented by the gravel in some places to the depth of 3 feet, and containing rolled pebbles of quartz, mountain-limestone, and sandstone of the carboniferous series, with chalk and flint.	10	No shells or vegetable remains in the grey marl. At 7 ft., *Elephas primigenius*, and down to 10 feet, where *horse, rhinoceros* and *deer* were also found.
Black marl, containing minute pebbles of chalk, very few flints; at the bottom two or three pieces of a fine-grained calcareous sandstone, similar specimens to which may be found in one of the adjacent beds of the red-marl series; no fragments derived from remote districts.	22½	At 11 feet, *bison* and *wolf*. At 12½ feet, *Elephant*. Between 13 and 14 feet, *Horse*. Between 14 and 15 feet, *Elephant* and *Duck*. Between 15 and 18 feet, *Bison* and *Wolf*. At 18 feet, *Bison* and *Horse*. The black marl abounds in shells, chiefly *Planorbis complanatus* and *Limnaea palustris*; and in vegetable remains. At 22½ feet, *Horse*.
Strong blue marl. Some clay nodules in this.	24	No bones, shells, or vegetable remains in these alternations.
Flint gravel in marl.	25	
Strong blue marl.		
Flint gravel in marl.	26½	
Red Keuper Marl.		

The black marl was not laminated; its surface was very irregular, and was penetrated by pipes and pockets of gravel from the bed above.

The bones obtained by the British Association Committee represented: *Elephas primigenius* (?), *Bison priscus*, *Bos primigenius*, *Bos* sp. (smaller than *longifrons* or *primigenius*), *Bos* sp., *Cervus* sp. In addition to these, Vernon Harcourt records: *Felis spelaea*, *Rhinoceros leptorhinus*, *Cervus elaphus*, *Equus fossilis* and *Canis lupus*.

Though no entire skeleton was found, some bones of the Wolf and Horse which articulated with one another lay together.

[7] *Phil. Mag.*, vol. vi, 1829, p. 225; and vol. vii, 1830, p. 1.
[8] *Rept. Brit. Assoc. for* 1907 (1908), p. 325; and *for* 1909 (1910), p. 177.

The 26 species of land and fresh-water mollusca were all of wide range; many are still living in the neighbourhood; and none afford any definite indications as to climate; neither do the few seeds of plants which were found.

It is possible that the Bielsbeck marl may extend northward, for there is in the Yorkshire Museum a tibia of *Elephas primigenius* found in digging for marl at Harswell, 3 miles to the north-west.

The sand and flint gravel overlying the marl at Bielsbeck is no doubt the same as that at Market Weighton, described in Chapter XVII. All that can be said as to the age of the fossiliferous marl is, that it is older than these.

CHAPTER XXIX.

POST-GLACIAL DEPOSITS.

I cannot refrain from remarking, that however visionary it may appear to hope for geological data sufficient to fix the chronology of the Deluge, should accurate and multiplied observations be extensively made upon the depth of sediment which rivers have deposited above the diluvium, and upon the depth of sediment which the same rivers are still accumulating, some approximation at least may be arrived at towards the solution of this question.

                              W. V. VERNON HARCOURT, 1830.

On 15th March, 1934, W. N. Edwards exhibited to the Hull Geological Society a number of dreikanters, or wind-facetted stones which he had found at Whitley, 8 miles south-south-west of Selby; and 50 feet above sea-level.

These objects are found in a pit excavated to a depth of 8 or 10 feet, in a deposit consisting almost entirely of sand. It contains a few stones near the bottom, and here and there the top is slightly gravelly; sometimes, but very rarely, a stone is found in the midst of the sand.

The dreikanters measure from a couple of inches to as many feet in length, and are usually very compact fine-grained sandstones. The sand with which they are associated has the red colour of disintegrated Bunter Sandstone. The grains are sub-angular, rather than markedly round, and average about 0.3 × 0.2 mm. in size.

In the next field to the south, there is a gravel pit in which thick beds of sand and gravel are seen dipping fairly steeply to the south-west.

The gravel consists of Carboniferous sandstones, mostly fairly fine-grained, but sometimes approaching millstone grit in coarseness. Occasionally encrinital chert and white flint with an ochreous patina are to be found.

There is no exposure to be seen between these two pits, and it is therefore difficult to tell whether the sand with the dreikanters is banked against the north side of the gravel; or whether it is an outcrop of that seen in the gravel pit.

Though the Bunter Sandstone was not seen beneath the gravels, it is known to come very near the surface at Whitley; and a buried ridge of it can be traced eastward at least as far as Rawcliffe.[1]

Quartzite boulders polished by wind-blown sand occur in the neighbourhood of Scunthorpe, Lincolnshire; and have been described by Archibald C. Dalton.[2] They are found over a large area, at heights of from 50 to over 200 feet above the sea.[3]

J. Wilfrid Jackson[4] has described and figured a number of facetted and wind-worn pebbles found near Manchester, and in the Wirral peninsula. He has shown that these Lancashire examples are post-glacial and pre-Neolithic in age.

We pass, finally, to the evidence of the latest considerable movement of the land, commonly known as the Neolithic Depression.

In his account of the Alexandra Dock Extension at Hull, already referred to in Chapter XVIII, Crofts has described a peat bed and the deposits overlying it (fig. 18).

The peat bed, the surface of which was 13 feet below sea-level, consisted of leaves, bark wood and stumps of oak, cherry, birch and hazel. In the overlying layer of clay, some cherries and a considerable quantity of cherry stones were found; also several small pieces of charcoal grouped together; but no trace of man.

The shells in the bed above included : *Cardium edule, Tellina solidula, Scrobicularia piperata, Utriculus obtusus, Rissoa ulvae, Littorina rudis, L. obtusata, Mytilus edulis, Pholas candida,* and *Nassa incrassata.*

A succession of beds, similar to the above, was seen in the excavations for the King George Dock.[5] Of all the organic remains found here, the most interesting is the femur of a pelican, figured and described by E. T. Newton.[6]

The peat and shell marl noted by Bisat at North Ferriby have been examined in detail by C. W. and E. V. Wright.[7] Twenty-six species of mollusca from the shell marl were identified by A. S. Kennard; of which the six following are not known living in the East Riding: *Acanthinula aculeata, A. lamellata, Vertigo pusilla, V. substriata, V. angustior* and *Columnella edentula.*

On the climatic evidence it is concluded that " the deposit cannot be later than the Beaker or Early Bronze Age, *circa* 1800 B.C."

On the south side of the Humber, peat occurs at Barton Water-side, 11 feet below high-water mark; and at New Holland a bed 2 to 4 feet thick lies beneath 27 feet of warp.[8]

---

[1]H. F. Parsons, *Proc. Yorks. Geol. Soc.*, vol. vi, 1879, p. 214; and vol. vii, 1881, p. 154, fig. 2.
[2]*The Naturalist*, 1912, p. 235.
[3]From information kindly supplied by Mr Harold E. Dudley, of Scunthorpe.
[4]*Manchester Memoirs*, vol. lxii, 1918, No. 9.
[5]*Trans. Hull Geol. Soc.*, vol. vi, 1922, p. 232.
[6]*The Naturalist*, 1928, p. 167.
[7]*The Naturalist*, 1933, p. 210.
[8]C. Reid, *Geology of Holderness*, 1885, p. 155.

Beds of peat similarly overlaid by warp have been met in borings at several places at the mouth of the River Ouse. Thus at Reedness, near Goole, almost 12 feet of "Black Moor Earth with some rotten wood, green moss (?) at the bottom," was passed through.[9] The base of this bed was 42 feet beneath the surface; or at least 30 feet below sea-level. At Goole, peat is found a few feet above the sea, but in a boring at the railway bridge between that town and Hook, a bed of it 18 feet thick was encountered; the bottom being about 25 feet below sea-level.

Borings made at the Selby Tannery[10] passed through peat at a depth of 6 or 7 feet; sand and loam with shells overlying it.

Further up the River Ouse, peat was found in a brickyard between Escrick and Riccall, lying under 19½ feet of warp and sand. This place is 25 feet above sea-level.

The buried peat beds of the Humber Estuary rest upon glacial deposits and are covered by warp which can be traced down the Lincolnshire coast at least as far as Mablethorpe.

It is evident, from the facts collected together in this chapter, that since glacial times there has been a depression of the land to the extent of at least 30 feet.

The effect of this depression can be detected far inland. At Clifton, York, two boreholes [11] were recently put down at the brink of the river (about 20 feet O.D.); the beds passed through are shown below:—

NO. 1 BORE.

							Thickness. Feet.	Depth. Feet.
Sand and clay,	...	...	...	...	...	...	37½	37½
Clay,	...	...	...	...	...	...	1	38½
Ballast,	...	...	...	...	...	...	2	40½
Sand,	...	...	...	...	...	...	11	51½
Bunter Sandstone.								

NO. 2 BORE.

						Thickness. Feet.	Depth. Feet.
Top soil,	...	...	...	...	...	4½	4½
River bed and Warp,	...	...	...	...	14½	19
Brown clayey sand,	...	...	...	...	14	33
Ballast,	...	...	...	...	...	5	38
Brown clay,	...	...	...	...	...	4	42
Yellow sand, very hard,	...	...	...	...	9½	51½
Bunter Sandstone.							

In No. 2 Bore, from a depth of 38 feet upward, there is a progressive reduction in the grade of the materials, from gravel through sand to warp, indicating a corresponding reduction in current velocity as the depression of the land increased. In this connection it is of interest to know that before 1757, when a weir and lock were built at Naburn, the tide reached Nun Monkton, 8 miles above York.[12]

[9] H. F. Parsons, *Proc. Yorks. Geol. Soc.*, vol. vi, 1879, p. 231.
[10] C. Fox-Strangways, *Water Supply of East Riding of Yorks.*, 1906, pp. 55, 56.
[11] For the details of these I am indebted to Mr C. N. Bromehead.
[12] G. Benson, *York; from its Origin to the End of the Eleventh Century*, 1911, p. 4.

The rivers appear now to be entering upon a period of erosion: on this point C. N. Bromehead[13] has made the following interesting observation. " Between Boston Spa and Newton Kyme the Wharfe is crossed by a Roman road; the exact site of the ford can be located with some precision, but even when the river is low the water there is something like 20 feet deep, while an easy fording can be made on a bed of gravel 200 yards up-stream. In other words, the river Wharfe has cut back this shallow about 200 yards in, say, 1700 years. It would be of interest to geologists and geographers if archaeologists would collect similar figures in as many localities as possible."

H. M. Platnauer[14] has recorded the results of a year's observation on the amount of total solids (soluble and insoluble) per litre of water taken from the River Ouse. From these it appears that when the river is at summer level, the amount of total solids is 223 milligrammes, whereas during flood, it is 211 milligrammes. The larger amount present under the former conditions is considered to be due to there then being a relatively greater quantity of matter in solution. During floods, the water tends to run off the land directly, instead of percolating through the soil; and therefore less matter is dissolved.

The amount of total solids brought down by the river during the year under observation was estimated to be 290,092 tons.

CHAPTER XXX.

THE CRUX.

Now, the crux of the Interglacial problem, so far as the British Islands are concerned, lies in the question whether these huge reservoirs [the North Sea and Irish Sea], after their first filling, were completely emptied during the supposed interglacial epoch of warmth . . . and were afterwards refilled for the later . . . glaciation.

To imagine, with the interglacialists, that the North Sea Basin was emptied of its ice-sheet, and was then filled again just far enough to influence the flow of the local ice, without extraneous re-invasion of our coast, seems to me an unwarranted sacrifice of the evidence to the idea.

In East Yorkshire, . . . if I read the sections aright, we can find no place into which a single mild interglacial epoch can be intercalated.

G. W. LAMPLUGH, 1906.

. . . my views on the subject . . . have not since been modified in any essential particular.

G. W. LAMPLUGH, 1913.

Lamplugh himself has stated clearly enough the idea to which interglacialists have, in his opinion, unwarrantably sacrificed the evidence.

13*A Scientific Survey of York and District*, prepared for the York Meeting of the Brit. Assoc., 1932, p. 13.
14*Ann. Rept. Yorks. Phil. Soc. for* 1898 (1899), Communications, p. 36.

" As opinion stands at present," he wrote, in 1906, " probably most geologists lean to the idea that the glaciation was interrupted by at least one interglacial epoch, during which the climate in any particular latitude became not less warm, and perhaps warmer, than it now is. This is the Interglacial hypothesis in its simplest form."[1]

Let us now examine the immolated evidence.

Lamplugh admitted that " there is, indeed, one deposit among those which I have examined, and only one, which at first sight seems to suggest inter-Glacial conditions. This is the estuarine silt or warp of Kirmington in North Lincolnshire, at from 60 to 80 feet above present sea-level, which, as mentioned in my previous address, is closely associated with true Glacial deposits, and marks a pronounced alternation of some kind. The presence of estuarine conditions at this spot is difficult to explain on any hypothesis, but particularly so if we suppose the whole country to have been ice-free at the time; and my former suggestion that the deposit was probably accumulated in an inlet between the bare land on the west and the temporarily receding ice-front on the east, still appears to be the most feasible, and has been strengthened by re-examinations of the section."[2]

Between the beginning of the Basement Clay glaciation and the epoch represented by the estuarine warp at Kirmington, the land had sunk 60 feet at least; so that the sea broke in upon it when the ice began to retreat. Lamplugh read the Kirmington section aright.

" Concurrently with this shrinkage of the East British ice-lobe there appears to have been a steady increase in the ice-caps which covered the broader upland tracks of the northern English counties. But all the evidence tends to show that the tongues descending eastward from these caps, from the time of the Basement clay onward to the close of the glaciation, were persistently prevented from passing freely outward by the presence of the main lobe in the North Sea Basin. Upon the shrinkage of the main lobe they were deflected southward along the hollow between it and the hilly land, which, in time, they filled again to a somewhat higher level than before, the inosculation of the upper and lower Purple boulder-clays with the stratified drifts marking the gradual stages in this process."[3]

This, Lamplugh's, account of the shrinkage is insufficient, considering the importance of the question involved: for it is the extent of this retreat which is, in his opinion, " the crux of the Interglacial problem, so far as the British Islands are concerned."

As to what happened after the ice began to withdraw, there is very little evidence in the Kirmington section beyond the fact that: " The estuarine bed is overlain by a coarse gravel of rolled flints, and in one part of the section this gravel is covered by 3 or 4 feet of red clay with far-travelled stones, resembling the Upper boulder-clay or Hessle Clay

[1]Rept. Brit. Assoc. for 1906 (1907), p. 533.
[2]C.-R., XIIe Sess. Congr. geol. internat., 1913, p. 429.
[3]op. cit., 1907, p. 545.

of Holderness."[4]   To gain a fuller insight into the history of the subsequent events, we must look elsewhere.

In the Alexandra Dock Extension at Hull, Crofts found the base of the Hessle Clay was at about 25 feet below O.D., and this is confirmed in the borings discussed by Wood and Rome.   It is clear, therefore, that after the period represented by the estuarine warp at Kirmington, and before the Hessle glaciation, erosion took place to the extent of 85 to 105 feet.   During this interval the North Sea Basin was so far emptied of its contents of ice, that the land rose about 100 feet; to a position at least 25 feet higher than that of to-day.

This is sufficient to refute Lamplugh's thesis; but it may be well to turn back and review the sequence of events from the beginning of the Glacial Period.

In 1919, Lamplugh[5] published a critical account of a boring put down at Kilnsea (25 feet O.D.).   It is of importance in that at 63 feet boulder clay was entered, which continued down to 127 feet from the surface.   This boulder clay he described as " firm rather sandy darkish purple boulder-clay, with crumbs of chalk "; and considered that it probably represents the Basement Clay of the coast section.   Beneath it came 3 feet of chocolate brown silty clay, without stones; lying on chalk-rubble.   The thickness of this chalk-rubble, which rested on the chalk, could not be readily estimated, but was more than 7 and less than 32 feet.   " A similar rubble exposed in the cliff and foreshore at Sewerby, on the south side of Flamborough Head, was found to contain small land-shells, indicating that it had been accumulated on a land-surface.   The presence of similar material at Kilnsea at over 100 ft. below sea level suggests a minimum measure for the elevation of the land above sea-level in East Yorkshire prior to the glaciation."

There is no mention of shells having been found in the sample of Basement Clay; but the diagnosis is supported by the record of " lead-coloured clay " met with at a depth of 109 feet (say, 95 feet below O.D.), in a boring[6] at Sunk Island.

In this connection it is interesting to recall a statement of Phillips, that at Ottringham Marsh, 13 miles east of Hull, a " layer of peat, one yard thick, was found *forty-one yards* beneath the surface; thirty-six yards of various diluvial matter lay beneath; and the chalk was found at the depth of seventy-eight yards."[7]

Fox-Strangways[8] has suggested that these measurements should be read as feet, not yards.   If there is any mistake here, it must be set down to the borer, for Phillips makes use of italics; and in the next paragraph he converts the measurements into feet in order to express the slope of the Chalk from Hessle to Ottringham in feet per mile.[9]

[8]*op. cit.*, p. 129.
[4]*op. cit.*, 1907, p. 544.
[5]*Summary of Progress Geol. Survey* for 1918 (1919), pp. 63-64.
[6]C. Fox-Strangways, *Water Supply East Riding of Yorks.*, 1906, p. 130.
[7]*Geol. of Yorks.*, 1st ed., 1829, p. 57.
[9]The result is misprinted in the first and second editions, and correctly stated in the third (p. 66).

The Ottringham Marsh and Kilnsea borings confirm each other and afford evidence of an old land surface at about 110 feet below O.D.

Thus we may say that at the beginning of the Glacial Period the land stood at least 100 feet higher above sea-level than it does to-day.

At Sewerby, the Basement Clay is seen overlying the old sea beach described in Chapter V. The land, therefore, had already sunk 100 feet below its original position, before the retreat of the Basement Clay ice.

But the estuarine bed at Kirmington shows that the land sank a further 100 feet; and the question arises whether the motion of the land from the beginning of the Glacial Period up to the time of the Kirmington deposit was always one of depression; or whether there was an uplift in the interval.

Clement Reid wrote: [10] " At Hornsea a thick bed of sand and gravel occurs below the sea-level, between two Boulder Clays, but this only having been proved by boring it is unsafe to correlate it with the Marine Bed. The borings made by Prof. Prestwich and Mr Smith at Kelsey Hill prove that there the base of the Gravel is at least 30 feet below the sea-level."

As to the age of the sand and gravel at Hornsea they certainly cannot be correlated with the sub-Basement Clay beach at Sewerby, for it stands above the present level of the sea. Of the two boulder clays between which they occur, it is of more consequence to ascertain the period of the upper. If it should be the Hessle Clay, then the presence of the sand and gravel merely confirms the evidence of a post-Purple and pre-Hessle uplift presented at the beginning of this chapter; but if this overlying clay is the Purple Boulder Clay, then we shall have here an indication of a pre-Purple or inter-Purple elevation.

A record of Clement Reid's throws light on this matter. " Opposite Mappleton [2½ miles S. of Hornsea] two divisions are seen, which appear to be the Hessle, and the Upper Purple Clay, the Lower Purple being below the beach line."[11]

The conclusion to be drawn from the evidence at Hornsea is, therefore, that the Upper Purple Clay overlies the sand and gravel; and that there was an elevation of the land after the retreat of the Basement Clay ice, and before the time of the Kirmington deposit.

We may now follow Reid, and go from Hornsea to Kelsey Hill.

All observers are agreed that the Hessle Clay overlies the Kelsey gravel. Reid saw also some Purple Clay, which, if it was *in situ*, confirms the evidence at Hornsea. Alternatively, if the overlying Purple Clay was pushed into its present position during the Hessle glaciation, the gravel must be of post-Purple age. This was the conclusion reached by Wood and Rome; for they agreed with Prestwich that the gravel at Paull was similar to that at Kelsey; and the Paull gravel they considered was the same as the sand underlying the Hessle Clay at Hessle.

The age of the Kelsey Hill gravel cannot be determined with certainty till the doubt about the overlying Purple Clay is resolved.

10 *Geol. of Holderness*, 1885, p. 66.
11 *op. cit.*, p. 34.

Meanwhile, it will not be unprofitable to examine Wood and Rome's inference more closely.

Their record of borings at the Hull Docks (fig. 12) shows the base of the sand under the Hessle Clay to be at about 46 feet below high-water mark, or 34 feet below O.D. But the base of the Kelsey gravel is at least 30 feet below sea-level at Kelsey Hill itself. It seems improbable, therefore, that the Hessle sand and the Kelsey gravel are one and the same.

The base of the gravel in the Old Pollard Farm boring is over 70 feet below the level of the sea. Whether it be the equivalent of the Kelsey Hill gravel or not, it seems most unlikely that it represents the \ Hessle sand at 34 feet.

We may close this chapter by setting down the conclusions at which we have arrived, and the evidence upon which they are based.

(i) *At the beginning of the Basement Clay glaciation, the land stood at least 100 feet higher above sea-level than it does now.*

This is proved by the evidence from the Kilnsea boring, as interpreted by Lamplugh; and from the boring at Ottringham Marsh recorded by Phillips.

(ii) *The land sank over 100 feet before the end of the Basement Clay glaciation.*

The old land surface in the Kilnsea and Ottringham borings is at least 100 feet below the present sea-level. The raised beach at Sewerby is 7½ feet above the same datum-line.
The Sewerby beach is covered by the Basement Clay.

(iii) *This movement of depression was not maintained throughout the whole of the Glacial Period: there was at least one period of elevation.*

There are four facts, any one of which is sufficient to prove that interglacial elevation took place.

(a) Sand and gravel occurs at Hornsea below the level of the Sewerby beach, and between two boulder clays.
(b) The gravel at Kelsey Hill extends at least 30 feet below O.D.
(c) At the Hull Docks there is sand at least 30 feet below sea-level; and this sand lies beneath boulder clay.
(d) Gravel was found over 70 feet below O.D., underneath boulder clay, in the Old Pollard Farm boring.

(iv) *There were two periods of interglacial elevation.*

This can be proved, without reference to boulder clays, thus: —

(a) The borings at the Hull Docks, recorded by Wood and Rome, reveal a bed of sand beneath boulder clay. The base of this sand is about 30 feet below O.D., and maintains this level from west to east for over three-quarters of a mile.

(b) Also at 30 feet below sea-level, gravel occurs at **Kelsey Hill**.

(c) There is gravel in the Old Pollard Farm boring, over 70 feet below O.D.

in (a), the deposit was evidently laid down in water which was nearing its base-level; in (b), this is not so. Therefore **(a)** and **(b)** probably do not belong to the same period.

(a) and (c) certainly do not belong to the same period.

(v) *Of the two movements of elevation; one took place between the end of the Upper Purple and the beginning of the Hessle glaciation.*

The following facts establish this conclusion : —

(a) The estuarine deposit at Kirmington extends from 60 to 80 feet above the present sea-level.
It overlies Purple Clay and is covered by Hessle Clay.

(b) The base of the Hessle clay was seen at about 25 feet below O.D. in the Alexandra Dock Extension, Hull; and in Wood and Rome's Hull Dock borings the sand beneath the Hessle Clay was found to extend at least 30 feet below the same datum.
Therefore, during the interval between (a) and (b), elevation took place to the extent of 90 to 110 feet.

(vi) *Of the two movements of elevation; the other probably took place between the Lower and Upper Purple glaciations.*

At least two facts point to this conclusion : —

(a) The Kelsey Hill gravel descends at least 30 feet below sea-level; as proved by Prestwich's boring. It rests upon Purple Clay, and Purple Clay has been seen above it.

(b) There is sand and gravel below sea-level, and between two boulder clays, at Hornsea. The overlying clay is probably Purple Boulder Clay.
At this epoch, therefore, the land stood not less than 30 feet higher above sea-level than it does to-day; or nearly 40 feet higher than it did at the time of the Sewerby beach.

Confirmatory evidence of two periods of interglacial erosion will be found in the next chapter.

CHAPTER XXXI.

CORRELATION.

The lithological similarities presented by these two Boulder-clays render it almost impossible to distinguish one from the other. . . . .

It is mainly, if not wholly, due to the introduction of Cretaceous rocks into the Trent basin at this stage that it is possible to classify the Boulder-clays and divide the deposits of the Pleistocene period into distinct lithological groups.

R. M. DEELEY, 1886.

The correlation of deposits at any two places cannot be effected until their sequence at each place has been ascertained. Before the succession of the glacial deposits in the Vale of York can be arrived at, a question of fundamental importance must be answered: Is the monoglacial hypothesis true; or are the interglacialists right when they assert that there was more than one glaciation during the Pleistocene period? Let us look into the matter, so far as it concerns this district.

We have seen that at one time ice blocked up the valley of the River Calder, forming a lake wherein the Horbury gravels were deposited. This lake is believed to have overflowed through a channel at 405 feet O.D.; the gravels at Rothwell Haigh are supposed to have been laid down under similar conditions, at 200 feet above sea-level. There is a channel, 70 feet above the sea, at Tadcaster, believed to be of glacial origin. Finally, there are the York and Escrick moraines at 50 feet O.D., the bases of which, according to some, are on the rock floor of the valley, 50 feet below sea-level.

The monoglacial interpretation of these things is, that during the Glacial Period a glacier moved down the Vale of York, until, in the latitude of Horbury, its lateral edge lay 405 feet above the sea, its terminal edge running, let us say, through Doncaster, 70 feet above O.D. Towards the end of the Glacial Period, the ice began to melt, and its lateral edge retreated 200 feet down the Pennine slope, while the terminal edge shrank back, say, to Snaith. At this time the Rothwell gravels were laid down. But the ice continued to retreat, and by the time the lateral edge of this same glacier had crept down a further 150 feet, the terminal edge had reached Escrick. Is this a true description of what happened?

At least three facts militate against the monoglacial hypothesis as applied to this area.

In the middle of the Vale of York there are three isolated hills jutting up through about 50 feet of detrital deposits, and rising over 100 feet above the surrounding country. They are Hambleton Hough and Brayton Barff, a few miles west of Selby, and the hill at the foot of which the village of Holme upon Spalding Moor stands.

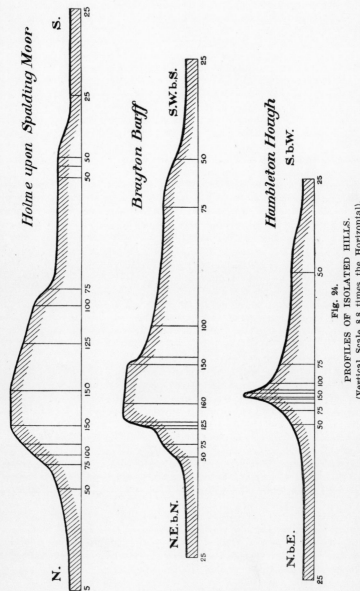

Fig. 24.

PROFILES OF ISOLATED HILLS.

(Vertical Scale 8.8 times the Horizontal).

Carvill Lewis met with a similar case in Ireland,[1] where, " before reaching Cappagh, limestone crags jut up in the centre of the valley, and glacial action is either absent or obscure. Boulders, however, are numerous."

The chance of limestone crags surviving unmodified after direct glacial action is small, and of sandstone hills, still less.

When a glacier passes directly over such protuberances it leaves them so far modified that the resulting products are given the name of *roches moutonnées*. It is typical of them that they present a smooth slope towards the direction from which the ice travelled, and a steeper slope to leeward. This consideration brings us to the first of our facts opposed to the monoglacial hypothesis, (i) The three hills are the wrong shape. The Vale of York ice came mainly from the north, but the gentler slope of the hills is to the south (fig. 24).

The second fact relates to the composition of the gravels. (ii) The gravel on the summits of Brayton Barff and of Holme consists almost wholly of Carboniferous sandstones. The gravel at the foot of Brayton Barff contains an admixture of Magnesian Limestone, while the low-level gravel at Holme is nearly all made up of Keuper Marl. The high- and low-level deposits are markedly different in composition.

In Chapter XIX we proved that the hill at Holme upon Spalding Moor had been carved out of the Trias, and the valley to the west of it filled in with detrital matter before the gravel on its summit was laid down. Herein we have an explanation of the absence of *moutonnée* structure. The sole of the glacier, which left the high-level gravels on its retreat, did not move along the rock floor, which is now 50 feet below sea-level, but upon the summit of the hills.

Our third fact confirms this conclusion. (iii) The summits of the isolated hills are, excluding the detritus, about the same height above O.D. At Holme, the height is 140 feet, and at Brayton Barff 150 feet. No particulars are available in the case of Hambleton Hough, as the thickness of the capping is unknown. Its whole height is 150 feet.

The hill to the west of York on which the village of Bilbrough stands may also be taken into consideration in this connection. Its height, without the detrital cap, is 130 feet above sea-level. But the York moraine passes over the top of it, so that, in this case, some allowance must be made for additional erosion during the Hessle glaciation.

In the Vale of York, then, we have to deal with two separate and distinct glaciers which passed down it. The sole of the earlier moved over a surface the height of which is indicated approximately by the top of Brayton Barff. After this glaciation, erosion took place to such an extent that at the next glaciation the ice moved along a plain over 100 feet lower. This later glacier never extended as far south as Holme or Brayton Barff, but left its terminal moraines at Escrick and York. When we remember that there is evidence in Holderness of such erosion between the Upper Purple and Hessle glaciations, the demonstration appears to be complete.

[1] *Glacial Geol. Gt. Britain and Ireland*, 1894, p. 141.

We are now in a better position to embark upon the process of correlating the deposits in the Vale of York. But with what shall we correlate them? The Holderness beds afford evidence of a period of interglacial erosion agreeing with that in the Vale of York, but this same erosion has produced an hiatus between the coast section and the deposits inland, which is not bridged till we pass southward into the valley of the River Trent.

The detailed examination of this region falls outside the scope of our enquiry. It will suffice to give a very brief account of the glacial geology of the Trent Valley, based on the work of R. M. Deeley.[2]

The succession established by Deeley is as follows :—

Newer Pleistocene	{ Later Pennine Boulder-clay. { Interglacial River-gravel.
Middle Pleistocene	{ Chalky Gravel. { Great Chalky Boulder-clay. { Melton Sand.
Older Pleistocene	{ Middle Pennine Boulder-clay. { Quartzose Sand. { Early Pennine Boulder-clay.

The Older Pleistocene.—The Early and Middle Pennine Boulder-clays are so similar lithologically that it is almost impossible to distinguish them from one another.

The Early Pennine Boulder-clay is a tough silty clay thickly studded with very small fragments of rock and occasional boulders. The stones include Keuper Marl, Liassic limestone (which is a local rock), quartzite, quartz and some Pennine rocks. Oolitic and Cretaceous rocks are absent.

The Middle Pennine Boulder-clay is almost, if not wholly, free from Cretaceous debris, but is frequently crammed full of Primary rocks from the Pennine axis. The stones are chiefly nodules of ironstone, Millstone Grit, Carboniferous chert with fossils, Coal Measures sandstone, white and black limestone and coal. "So far as my observations go," says Deeley, "the mass of this clay was formed in the path of the great glaciers which came down the valleys of the Derwent, Wye, and Dove, and crossed the partially submerged valley of the Trent in the direction of the Charnwood Hills. In addition to the ice-stream which came down the northern and western tributaries of the Trent, the press of ice in the Irish Sea seems to have led to the deflection of the Scotch and Cumbrian glaciers into the western portion of the Trent basin, for at Burton-on-Trent there are in the Pennine Boulder-clay erratics entirely foreign to this area."

The intervening Quartzose Sand is very pebbly and contains quartzites and quartz, brown sandstone, brown haematite, Coal Measures sandstone, white, yellow and purple clay, but no flint. At some places it contains streaks of lignite.

The Middle Pleistocene.—In the Melton Sand, flints suddenly make their appearance in great numbers for the first time. "Unfortunately no section has yet been found showing the passage of Older Pleistocene Boulder-clay into Middle Pleistocene sand. Indeed, there appears to have been somewhat of a break between these two epochs, perhaps partly due to temporary elevation and subaerial denudation. This break, which partakes of the nature of an unconformity, is clearly shown in many sections." It will be noted that this break occurs between the end of the Older and the beginning of the Middle Pleistocene; in the Middle Pleistocene epoch itself there is no break.

[2] *Q.J.G.S.*, vol. xlii, 1886, p. 437.

The Great Chalky Boulder-clay in the Trent valley is an extension westward of that seen in East Anglia. It contains chalk and flint in abundance, together with Pennine rocks derived from the Older Pennine deposits over which the ice passed.

It is this intrusion of boulder clay containing chalk, obviously derived from the east, which makes it possible to differentiate between the Older and Newer Pleistocene deposits, both of which are composed of materials from a westerly Pennine source. The Great Chalky Boulder-clay extends up the Trent valley at least as far as Hanbury, north-west of Burton-on-Trent, where it is over 400 feet above sea-level.

The Chalky Gravel was deposited during the retreat of the ice which formed the Great Chalky Boulder-clay : it does not call for detailed consideration here.

The Newer Pleistocene.—The beginning of this epoch is characterised by the formation of the Interglacial River-gravel, giving rise to terraces which stand from 30 to about 74 feet above the present flood-level of the River Trent. The gravel is composed of a mixture of materials derived from the pre-existing glacial deposits.

At Allenton, not quite three miles south of Derby, this Interglacial gravel has a sandy top overlain by about 7 feet of sandy clay. In the sand immediately above the gravel, plant remains have been found, together with bones, mostly of Hippopotamus, but among which were some of Elephant and Rhinoceros.[3] The plants indicated a moist meadow or swampy ground, and a temperate climate.

The Later Pennine Boulder-clay was so named by Deeley, but " it must not be supposed that Pennine rocks always form a large percentage of the deposit; indeed, it is frequently almost wholly formed from the subjacent rocks, with the addition of a few Pennine, Cambrian, or even Cumbrian erratic boulders. My reason for calling it Later Pennine is more to mark the return of local ice-action, interrupted during the Middle Pleistocene epoch by the formation of the Great Chalky Boulder-clay, than to indicate its lithological characteristics." He also states that there is nothing to prove that the deposits included under this name " might not have been formed during more than one interval of cold occurring while the deposition of the Interglacial River-gravels took place."

As to the distribution of all these boulder clays, it appears, as a general rule, that those " of Older or Middle Pleistocene age will be found to occupy lower and lower positions in the valleys the nearer they approach the present water-courses. It would therefore seem that the broader features of hill and valley were sketched out in preglacial times, and that Newer Pleistocene erosion has, after removing the greater portion of the older Boulder-clays from the low-lying areas where they occurred, commenced to widen and deepen the old valleys."

Out of all this two facts emerge which are of immediate application to our present problem of correlation.

(i) There are two breaks in the succession. The first occurs between the end of the Older and the beginning of the Middle Pleistocene epoch ; the second is represented by the Interglacial River-gravel at the bottom of the Newer Pleistocene. We can at once place these side by side with those in the Holderness sequence, namely, that between the Lower and Upper Purple and that between the Upper Purple and Hessle Boulder Clays. At the same time, we can equate the latest boulder clay in the Trent Basin with the latest in the Vale of York. The result stands thus : —

[3] *Q.J.G.S.*, vol. lii, 1896, p. 497.

TRENT BASIN.	VALE OF YORK AND HOLDERNESS.
Later Pennine Boulder Clay.	Glacier of York and Escrick moraines (=Hessle Clay of Holderness).
Interglacial River-gravel.	
~~*~*~*~*~*~*~*~*~*~*~*~*~*~*~*~*~*~	*~*~*~*~*~*~*~*~*~*~*~*~*~*~*~*~*~*~*~
Chalky Gravel.	
Great Chalky Boulder Clay.	Upper Purple Boulder Clay.
Melton Sand.	
~~*~*~*~*~*~*~*~*~*~*~*~*~*~*~*~*~*~	*~*~*~*~*~*~*~*~*~*~*~*~*~*~*~*~*~*~*~
Middle Pennine Boulder Clay.	Lower Purple Boulder Clay.
Quartzose Sand.	
Early Pennine Boulder Clay.	

(ii) The Interglacial River-gravel of the Trent contains the remains of Hippopotamus and Elephant. Bones of the same animals were found in similar deposits at Leeds, which are themselves like those at Woodlesford.

According to Gilligan, " a great interval of time must be represented between the period when the Rothwell gravels and clays were formed and that at which those at Woodlesford were deposited." This great interval of time is already indicated in the table, where it stands for that period of gradual erosion between the Upper Purple and Hessle glaciations. Before embodying these results in the table, we may cast our eye over it and note what has been accomplished so far.

Of the four boulder clays in the left-hand column, all but one have been matched, and of the Holderness boulder clays only one remains to be accounted for. The Basement Clay of Holderness is, therefore, the equivalent of the Early Pennine Boulder Clay in the Trent Valley. The collected results now appear as follows : —

TRENT BASIN.	VALE OF YORK AND HOLDERNESS.
Later Pennine Boulder Clay.	Glacier of York and Escrick moraines (=Hessle Clay of Holderness).
Interglacial River-gravel.	Leeds Hippopotamus deposit, and Woodlesford beds.
~~*~*~*~*~*~*~*~*~*~*~*~*~*~*~*~*~*~	*~*~*~*~*~*~*~*~*~*~*~*~*~*~*~*~*~*~*~
Chalky Gravel.	Rothwell Haigh gravels.
Great Chalky Boulder Clay.	Upper Purple Boulder Clay.
Melton Sand.	
~~*~*~*~*~*~*~*~*~*~*~*~*~*~*~*~*~*~	*~*~*~*~*~*~*~*~*~*~*~*~*~*~*~*~*~*~*~
Middle Pennine Boulder Clay.	Lower Purple Boulder Clay.
Quartzose Sand.	
Early Pennine Boulder Clay.	Basement Boulder Clay of Holderness.

Let us now turn to consider what other deposits in the Vale of York can be associated with those already accommodated in the table.

There can be little doubt that the Rothwell beds are part of that great sheet of gravel, sand, and clay, remains of which are seen on the top of Brayton Barff and the hill at Holme upon Spalding Moor; and in the high-level beds against the slope of the Wolds, from Mill Hill northward to Throstle Wood, we recognise the eastern margin of this same sheet. All these, therefore, and the hanging tributary at Goodmanham, together with the valleys at Millington and Bishop Wilton mentioned in Chapter XX, must be entered in the table beside the Rothwell Haigh gravels. The Wingate Hill beds also find a place here.

Up to this point the stages in the process of correlation have facts to justify them. The majority of the deposits on the west side of the Vale of York, mentioned in Chapter XXI, remain to be considered, but, in the absence of sections showing the direct superposition of one upon another, they cannot be discussed with much profit. The Dewsbury boring, recorded by J. W. Davis, is perhaps in different case. Here, it will be remembered, two distinctly different layers of boulders were passed through, the upper consisting principally of sandstone and the lower of crystalline rocks. These may be assigned respectively to the top and bottom of Deeley's Older Pleistocene, but not with impunity, for, so far from there being anything between them to correspond with the Quartzose Sand, the two Dewsbury gravels merge gradually into one another.

For the rest, those high-level deposits south of Leeds, which are believed to have been laid down in lakes whose eastern margin was a glacier which had travelled over Stainmore and then down the Vale of York, must belong to the Upper Purple glaciation, for the shape of Brayton Barff and the hill at Holme show that neither before nor since that time did any such glacier, coming from the north, pass so far southward.

For the same reason, the deposit at Balby cannot be a product of the Stainmore ice. Its materials must have come from over the Pennines to the west of that place, and this conclusion, we have seen, is supported by the petrographical evidence.

Finally, we return to the problem of the Kelsey Hill gravel. If Clement Reid's overlying Purple Clay is *in situ*, the Kelsey gravel becomes the equivalent of the Melton Sand.

The correlation table now stands thus:—

TRENT BASIN.	VALE OF YORK AND HOLDERNESS.
Later Pennine Boulder Clay.	Glacier of York and Escrick moraines (=Hessle Clay of Holderness).
Interglacial River-gravel.	Leeds Hippopotamus deposit, and Woodlesford beds.
Chalky Gravel.	Rothwell Haigh gravels; high-level deposits of Brayton Barff, Holme, Wingate Hill and the Wolds; Millington and Bishop Wilton valleys.
Great Chalky Boulder Clay.	Upper Purple Boulder Clay.
Melton Sand.	(?) Kelsey Hill gravels.
Middle Pennine Boulder Clay.	Lower Purple Boulder Clay and (?) Balby deposit.
Quartzose Sand. Early Pennine Boulder Clay.	Basement Boulder Clay of Holderness.

Without the Interglacial Theory, the history of the deposits in the Vale of York cannot be unravelled.

Sedgwick wrote, in 1825: " The waters have, therefore, during successive ages, been propelled into the recesses of the coast by different forces, and up different systems of inclined planes; and must in consequence have ascended to different levels."

The truth of this has been demonstrated.

APPENDICES.

A. THE OCCURRENCE OF MANGANESE.

In the course of this book, deposits blackened with manganese dioxide have been noted at the following places:—

(i) Between Cave and Holme upon Spalding Moor; seen by Vernon Harcourt (Chap. XVII).

(ii) At Thorpe-le-Street; observed by myself (Chap. XVII).

(iii) At Woodlesford; noted by Gilligan (Chap. XXII).

(iv) On the floor of Kirkdale Cave; as recorded by Buckland (Chap. XXVIII).

As it is very probable this distribution of manganese may hereafter be found to have a chronological significance, it may be well to place on record some other observations of the same kind.

(v) At Boston Spa, just above the floor of the pit near the Gasworks, I noticed the gravel was coated black; although the matter was not tested chemically, there is little doubt the colouring was due to manganese and not carbon.

(vi) At Fulford, York, on the left bank of the river, there are gravel pits, now grassed over. J. E. Clark,[1] who examined them carefully at the time they were being worked, states: "They generally present a section 15 to 30 feet in height. The most peculiar feature is a bed of Manganese, 25 feet below the surface at the point worked in 1877. It was exposed at two positions 100 yards apart. The bed containing it consisted of loose dry pebbles, and was one foot thick. The upper five inches looked as if encrusted with soot (Manganese dioxide, MnO_2), whilst the pebbles beneath were brown with the sesqui-oxide, Mn_2O_3. This also appeared in the bed above, as much as 5 feet being affected in places. Below this, iron gave a corresponding ochreous coating, although the matrix was clayey. The workmen said they met the ' soot ' in all parts, although it occasionally thinned out." Samples, sifted free from coarse sand, were found to contain about 60 per cent. of manganese dioxide. Similar manganiferous gravel was seen on the opposite side of the river.

(vii) At Lingerfield, two miles north-west of Knaresborough, there was, in 1933, the most striking example I have seen so far of such gravel.

The face of the pit is about 20 feet in height, and shows coarse gravel throughout, with, occasionally, thin partings of coarse current-bedded sand, particularly near the bottom. The main manganiferous part was seen about one-third of the way up the section. It was a horizontal

[1]*Proc. Yorks. Geol. Soc.*, vol. vii, 1881, p. 426.

lens-shaped mass, 36 feet long, and 18 inches thick in the middle. The upper surface was flat. It consisted of coarse gravel, coated black with oxide of manganese (tested chemically). The pebbles varied in size from less than half-an-inch up to 4 inches. Immediately below this basin-shaped mass there was more gravel, exactly the same as that described but without the black coating. Immediately above, there was a layer of sand 10 inches thick, and then gravel. Just above the floor of the pit the manganese occurs sporadically, following the current-bedding of the sand partings.

A workman told me the lens-shaped manganiferous deposit had been seen ever since the pit was opened, but when re-visited in June 1934 it showed signs of dying out, and was not nearly so extensive and well defined as when seen in August and September of the previous year.

The secretion of manganese by micro-organisms has been very fully studied by George A. Thiel (*Econ. Geol.*, vol. xx, 1925, pp. 301-310).

B. THE FAUNA OF KELSEY HILL.

The following lists are compiled mainly from those of Reid, Sheppard and Stather, with the addition of a few records from *The Naturalist*.

INVERTEBRATA.

Terebratulina caput-serpentis d'Orb.
Balanus crenatus Brug.
Anomia ephippium L.
Astarte borealis Chemn.
A. compressa Mont.
Cardium edule L.
C. exiguum Gmel.
Corbicula fluminalis Müller.
Corbula gibba Olivi.
Cyprina islandica Lam.
Cytherea chione L.
Donax vittatus Da C.
Mactra solida L.
M. subtruncata Da C.
Mya arenaria L.
M. truncata L.
Mytilus edulis L.
Nucula nuculeus L.
Ostrea edulis L.
Pecten islandicus Müller
Pholas crispata L.
Saxicava arctica L.
Scrobicularia plana Da C.
Solen siliqua ? L.
Tapes decussata L.
Tellina balthica L.
T. obliqua J. Sow.
Venus gallina L.
Dentalium entalis L.
Buccinum undatum L.
Hydrobia ulvae Pen.

Lacuna crassior Mont
L. vincta Mont.
Littorina rudis Maton
L. littorea L.
L. squalida B. & S.
Murex erinaceus L.
Nassa reticulata L.
Natica alderi Forb.
N. catena Da C.
N. clausa B. & S.
N. groenlandica Beck.
N. islandica Gmel.
Pleurotoma nebula Mont.
P. pyramidalis Strom.
P. turricula Mont.
Purpura lapillus L.
Rissoa labiosa Mont.
Scalaria communis Lan.
Trochus cinerarius L
Trophon antiquus L.
T. bamffius Mont.
T. gracilis Da C.
T. scalariformis Gould
Turritella terebra L.
Hima incrassata Müller.
Patella vulgata L.
Bitium reticulatum ? Mont.
Polyzoon.
Spines of *Echinus.*
Claw of Crab.

VERTEBRATA.

Elephas primigenius Blum.
Cervus elaphus L.
Rangifer tarandus L.
Bison priscus Boj.

Rhinoceros leptorhinu. Cuv.
Trichechus rosmarus L.
Phoca ? vitulina L.
Gadus morrhua ? L.

VERTEBRATA FROM BURSTWICK.

Elephas primigenius Blum.
Bos primigenius Boj.
B. taurus L.

Megaceros hibernicus Owen
Cervus elaphus L.
Hyaena sp. ?.

INDEX.